Author:
Ruth M. Young, M.S. Ed.
Elementary Science
Consultant

Illustrator:
Kerry Manwaring
Keith Vasconcelles

Editors:
Evan D. Forbes, M.S. Ed.
Walter Kelly, M.A.
Carol Amato, M.A.

Senior Editor:
Sharon Coan, M.S. Ed.

Art Direction:
Elayne Roberts

Product Manager:
Phil Garcia

Imaging:
Alfred Lau

Photo Cover Credit:
Images provided by PhotoDisc
©1994

Research:
Bobbie Johnson

Publishers:
Rachelle Cracchiolo, M.S. Ed.
Mary Dupuy Smith, M.S. Ed.

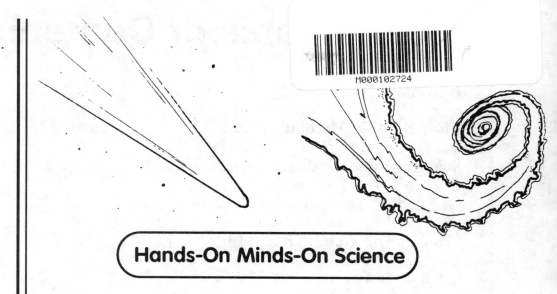

Hands-On Minds-On Science

Space

Intermediate

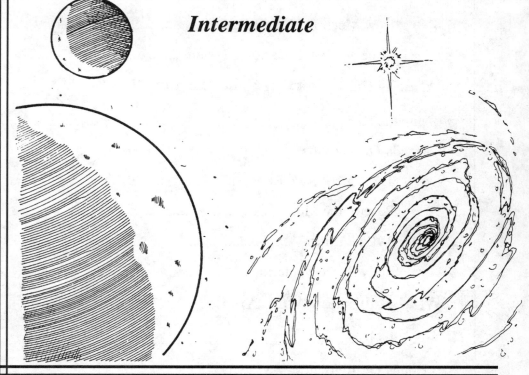

Teacher Created Materials, Inc.
P.O. Box 1040
Huntington Beach, CA   92647
©1994 Teacher Created Materials, Inc.
Made in U.S.A.

ISBN-1-55734-639-9

Table of Contents

Table of Contents *(cont.)*

Introduction

What Is Science

What is science to children? Is it something that they know is part of their world? Is it a textbook in the classroom? Is it a tadpole changing into a frog? A sprouting seed, a rainy day, a boiling pot, a turning wheel, a pretty rock, or a moonlit sky? Is science fun and filled with wonder and meaning? What is science to children?

Science offers you and your eager students opportunities to explore the world around you and to make connections between the things you experience. The world becomes your classroom, and you, the teacher, a guide.

Science can, and should, fill children with wonder. It should cause them to be filled with questions and the desire to discover the answers to their questions. And, once they have discovered answers, they should be actively seeking new questions to answer.

The books in this series give you and the students in your classroom the opportunity to learn from the whole of your experience—the sights, sounds, smells, tastes, and touches, as well as what you read, write about, and do. This whole-science approach allows you to experience and understand your world as you explore science concepts and skills together.

What Is Space?

Space is the boundless expanse in which our universe moves and all known things exist, including our Earth. This book covers only a few of the many topics regarding space. These include the sun, the planets of our solar system, the Great Space Race, early space vehicles, space stations, the space shuttle, and the phases of the moon. Like a search for a legendary place, the study of space can increase our knowledge and insight of this last, great frontier, and turn myths into realities. To hold a moon rock in our hands, to see the charred space capsule in a museum, to meet real astronauts, to try on a real space suit is to be captured by a desire to learn more about these uncharted territories.

Our studies of space over the last 35 years—and much remains to be learned—have revealed amazing things, from the proof that the moon is solid to the discovery in 1994 of the positive existence of black holes and the existence of the amino acid glycine (the building block of life) at a location other than the earth. Does this mean life exists elsewhere? Every bit we learn whets our appetite to know more about what exists out there while sharpening our impulse to go find out. Space is indeed a proper study for all humankind.

The Scientific Method

The "scientific method" is one of several creative and systematic processes for proving or disproving a given question, following an observation. When the "scientific method" is used in the classroom, a basic set of guiding principles and procedures is followed in order to answer a question. However, real world science is often not as rigid as the "scientific method" would have us believe.

This systematic method of problem solving will be described in the paragraphs that follow.

1 Make an OBSERVATION.

The teacher presents a situation, gives a demonstration, or reads background material that interests students and prompts them to ask questions. Or students can make observations and generate questions on their own as they study a topic.

Example: Have students weigh themselves on a scale.

2 Select a QUESTION to investigate.

In order for students to select a question for a scientific investigation, they will have to consider the materials they have or can get, as well as the resources (books, magazines, people, etc.) actually available to them. You can help them make an inventory of their materials and resources, either individually or as a group.

Tell students that in order to successfully investigate the questions they have selected, they must be very clear about what they are asking. Discuss effective questions with your students. Depending upon their level, simplify the question or make it more specific.

Example: How much would you weigh on other planets in our solar system and on the moon?

3 Make a PREDICTION (Hypothesis).

Explain to students that a hypothesis is a good guess about what the answer to a question will probably be. But they do not want to make just any arbitrary guess. Encourage students to predict what they think will happen and why.

In order to formulate a hypothesis, students may have to gather more information through research.

Have students practice making hypotheses with questions you give them. Tell them to pretend they have already done their research. You want them to write each hypothesis so it follows these rules:

1. It is to the point.
2. It tells what will happen, based on what the question asks.
3. It follows the subject/verb relationship of the question.

Example: I think I would weigh less on other planets and on the moon.

The Scientific Method *(cont.)*

4   Develop a **PROCEDURE** to test the hypothesis.

The first thing students must do in developing a procedure (the test plan) is to determine the materials they will need.

They must state exactly what needs to be done in step-by-step order. If they do not place their directions in the right order, or if they leave out a step, it becomes difficult for someone else to follow their directions. A scientist never knows when other scientists will want to try the same experiment to see if they end up with the same results!

Example: Once students know their own weight, they will multiply it by the surface gravity of other planets and the moon to find their new weight.

5   Record the **RESULTS** of the investigation in written and picture form.

The results (data collected) of a scientific investigation are usually expressed two ways—in written form and in picture form. Both are summary statements. The written form reports the results with words. The picture form (often a chart or graph) reports the results so the information can be understood at a glance.

Example: The results of this investigation can be recorded on a data-capture sheet provided (pages 21-22).

6   State a **CONCLUSION** that tells what the results of the investigation mean.

The conclusion is a statement which tells the outcome of the investigation. It is drawn after the student has studied the results of the experiment, and it interprets the results in relation to the stated hypothesis. A conclusion statement may read something like either of the following: "The results show that the hypothesis is supported," or "The results show that the hypothesis is not supported." Then restate the hypothesis if it was supported or revise it if it was not supported.

Example: The hypothesis that stated "I would weigh less on other planets and the moon" is supported (or not supported).

7   Record **QUESTIONS, OBSERVATIONS,** and **SUGGESTIONS** for future investigations.

Students should be encouraged to reflect on the investigations that they complete. These reflections, like those of professional scientists, may produce questions that will lead to further investigations.

Example: Why does weight change when I am not on the Earth?

Science-Process Skills

Even the youngest students blossom in their ability to make sense out of their world and succeed in scientific investigations when they learn and use the science-process skills. These are the tools that help children think and act like professional scientists.

The first five process skills on the list below are the ones that should be emphasized with young children, but all of the skills will be utilized by anyone who is involved in scientific study.

Observing

It is through the process of observation that all information is acquired. That makes this skill the most fundamental of all the process skills. Children have been making observations all their lives, but they need to be made aware of how they can use their senses and prior knowledge to gain as much information as possible from each experience. Teachers can develop this skill in children by asking questions and making statements that encourage precise observations.

Communicating

Humans have developed the ability to use language and symbols which allow them to communicate not only in the "here and now" but also over time and space as well. The accumulation of knowledge in science, as in other fields, is due to this process skill. Even young children should be able to understand the importance of researching others' communications about science and the importance of communicating their own findings in ways that are understandable and useful to others. The space journal and the data-capture sheets used in this book are two ways to develop this skill.

Comparing

Once observation skills are heightened, students should begin to notice the relationships between things that they are observing. *Comparing* means noticing similarities and differences. By asking how things are alike and different or which is smaller or larger, teachers will encourage children to develop their comparison skills.

Ordering

Other relationships that students should be encouraged to observe are the linear patterns of seriation (order along a continuum: e.g., rough to smooth, large to small, bright to dim, few to many) and sequence (order along a time line or cycle). By ranking graphs, time lines, cyclical and sequence drawings, and by putting many objects in order by a variety of properties, students will grow in their abilities to make precise observations about the order of nature.

Categorizing

When students group or classify objects or events according to logical rationale, they are using the process skill of categorizing. Students begin to use this skill when they group by a single property such as color. As they develop this skill, they will be attending to multiple properties in order to make categorizations; the animal classification system, for example, is one system students can categorize.

Science-Process Skills *(cont.)*

Relating
Relating, which is one of the higher-level process skills, requires student scientists to notice how objects and phenomena interact with one another and the change caused by these interactions. An obvious example of this is the study of chemical reactions.

Inferring
Not all phenomena are directly observable, because they are out of humankind's reach in terms of time, scale, and space. Some scientific knowledge must be logically inferred based on the data that is available. Much of the work of paleontologists, astronomers, and those studying the structure of matter is done by inference.

Applying
Even very young, budding scientists should begin to understand that people have used scientific knowledge in practical ways to change and improve the way we live. It is at this application level that science becomes meaningful for many students.

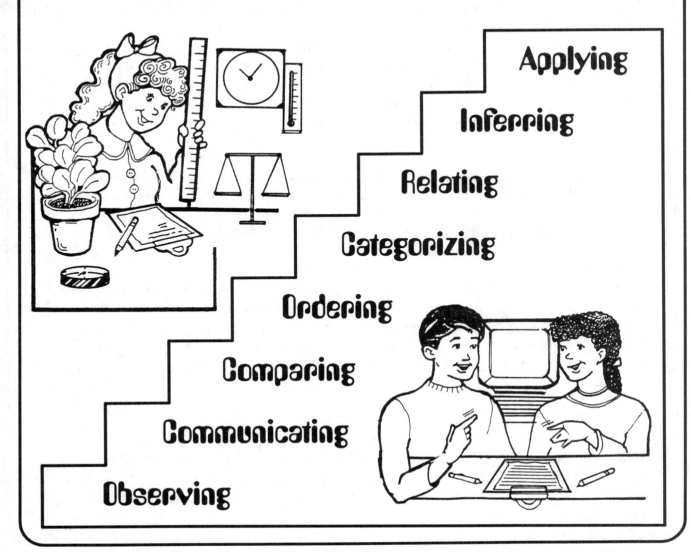

Organizing Your Unit

Designing a Science Lesson

In addition to the lessons presented in this unit, you will want to add lessons of your own, lessons that reflect the unique environment in which you live, as well as the interests of your students. When designing new lessons or revising old ones, try to include the following elements in your planning:

Question

Pose a question to your students that will guide them in the direction of the experiment you wish to perform. Encourage all answers, but you want to lead the students towards the experiment you are going to be doing. Remember, there must be an observation before there can be a question. (Refer to The Scientific Method, pages 5-6.)

Setting the Stage

Prepare your students for the lesson. Brainstorm to find out what students already know. Have children review books to discover what is already known about the subject. Invite them to share what they have learned.

Materials Needed for Each Group or Individual

List the materials each group or individual will need for the investigation. Include a data-capture sheet when appropriate.

Procedure

Make sure students know the steps to take to complete the activity. Whenever possible, ask them to determine the procedure. Make use of assigned roles in group work. Create (or have your students create) a data-capture sheet. Ask yourself, "How will my students record and report what they have discovered? Will they tally, measure, draw, or make a checklist? Will they make a graph? Will they need to preserve specimens?" Let students record results orally, using a video or audio tape recorder. For written recording, encourage students to use a variety of paper supplies such as poster board or index cards. It is also important for students to keep a journal of their investigation activities. Journals can be made of lined and unlined paper. Students can design their own covers. The pages can be stapled or be put together with brads or spiral binding.

Extensions

Continue the success of the lesson. Consider which related skills or information you can tie into the lesson, like math, language arts skills, or something being learned in social studies. Make curriculum connections frequently and involve the students in making these connections. Extend the activity, whenever possible, to home investigations.

Closure

Encourage students to think about what they have learned and how the information connects to their own lives. Prepare space journals using directions on page 78. Provide an ample supply of blank and lined pages for students to use as they complete the Closure activities. Allow time for students to record their thoughts and pictures in their journals.

Organizing Your Unit *(cont.)*

Structuring Student Groups for Scientific Investigations

Using cooperative learning strategies in conjunction with hands-on and discovery learning methods will benefit all the students taking part in the investigation.

Cooperative Learning Strategies

1. In cooperative learning, all group members need to work together to accomplish the task.
2. Cooperative learning groups should be heterogeneous.
3. Cooperative learning activities need to be designed so that each student contributes to the group and individual group members can be assessed on their performance.
4. Cooperative learning teams need to know the social as well as the academic objectives of a lesson.

Cooperative Learning Groups

Groups can be determined many ways for the scientific investigations in your class. Here is one way of forming groups that has proven to be successful in intermediate classrooms.

- **The Commander**—scientist in charge of reading directions and setting up equipment.
- **The Pilot**—scientist in charge of carrying out directions (can be more than one student).
- **The Mission Specialist**—scientist in charge of recording all of the information.
- **The Payload Specialist**—scientist who translates notes and communicates findings.

If the groups remain the same for more than one investigation, require each group to vary the people chosen for each job. All group members should get a chance to try each job at least once.

Using Centers for Scientific Investigations

Set up stations for each investigation. To accommodate several groups at a time, stations may be duplicated for the same investigation. Each station should contain directions for the activity, all necessary materials (or a list of materials for investigators to gather), a list of words (a word bank) which students may need for writing and speaking about the experience, and any data-capture sheets or needed materials for recording and reporting data and findings.

Station-to-Station Activities are on pages 75-76. Model and demonstrate each of the activities for the whole group. Have directions at each station. During the modeling session, have a student read the directions aloud while the teacher carries out the activity. When all students understand what they must do, let small groups conduct the investigations at the centers. You may wish to have a few groups working at the centers while others are occupied with other activities. In this case, you will want to set up a rotation schedule so all groups have a chance to work at the centers.

Assign each team to a station, and after they complete the task described, help them rotate in a clockwise order to the other stations. If some groups finish earlier than others, be prepared with another unit-related activity to keep students focused on main concepts. After all rotations have been made by all groups, come together as a class to discuss what was learned.

Just the Facts

Our solar system has fascinated people for thousands of years. Long ago, people thought that the sun, moon, and the planets all moved around the Earth. This is called the *geocentric system*. If you watch the sky over a long period, it does appear that everything revolves around the earth. You see the sun rising in the east and setting in the west every day. The moon, stars, and planets appear to travel this same route daily. If you record the way the moon moves, you can see that the it gradually moves eastward day by day, changing its shape as it does so. Constellations gradually change as the Earth moves through seasons; new ones appear in the east and old ones disappear in the west. At first, most people and scientists believed in the geocentric system. Only a few were brave enough to challenge the theory and dared to suggest that the Earth and other planets revolved around the sun. Thanks to brave scientists such as Copernicus (in 1514) and Galileo (in 1609), people slowly began to accept the idea that the Earth is not the center of the planets, but that everything in our solar system revolves around the sun. The history of these two scientists is very interesting, especially since they were both in danger of losing their lives because of their beliefs.

There are nine planets in our solar system, all revolving in the same direction around the sun, but at different distances and speeds. Let us take an imaginary trip to each of these planets:

Mercury   This planet is closest to the sun and therefore is the hottest. It takes only 88 days for Mercury to go around the sun, but its day is 59 Earth days long. This planet is just slightly larger than our moon. Since there is no atmosphere, pictures of its surface can be taken by satellites. Mercury's temperatures range from 800°F (407°C) in the sunlight to -300°F (-183°C) in the dark. Mercury has no moons.

Venus   Nearly the same size as the Earth, this planet is covered with clouds that are so thick that its surface is not visible through a telescope. It frequently appears in the evening or early morning sky looking like a bright white star. Its atmosphere is mostly sulfuric acid and carbon dioxide and is extremely dense. The sun's heat is trapped by the clouds so temperatures are about 900°F (460°C) on the surface. If you landed on Venus, you would be dissolved, roasted, and crushed by its atmosphere. There are mountains and lowlands on its surface. This planet rotates once every 243 Earth days and travels around the sun in 225 days. Venus has no moons.

Earth   What a beautiful blue jewel of a planet we live on. Our atmosphere protects us from the sun's heat and harmful rays, permitting just the right amount of sunlight through to provide plants with the energy they need to grow. About 71% of the Earth is covered by water, some of which is frozen in the polar ice caps in the Arctic and Antarctica. We are located in the "life zone" of the solar system, where our planet is not too hot or too cold for life to exist. Earth rotates once every 24 hours and takes about 365 days to travel around the sun. There is one moon orbiting our planet.

Just the Facts *(cont.)*

Mars   This planet was named after the Roman god of war since it looks like a red star in the night sky. This red color comes from the rocks on its surface that have a great deal of iron in them and that "rust" in the moisture in Mars' thin atmosphere. It is about half the size of Earth, but has a day that is about the same length as ours. Mars' year is 687 Earth days long. There are two moons orbiting this planet. They are very small and are not shaped like a sphere. Some scientists think they may be asteroids that strayed close to Mars and were trapped in orbit. Mars has polar ice caps and seasons like Earth, which change as the planet moves around the sun. Two unmanned satellites, *Viking I* and *II*, landed on Mars in 1975 to photograph the surface, record the temperature, test the soil, and conduct other experiments. All of this was done through commands sent to the Vikings from people on Earth. No life was found on the planet, but pictures show signs that running water was once there, so there may have been life at one time. This water is now frozen in the soil and polar ice caps of the planet. Someday, humans will go to Mars to explore it and possibly set up a base where people can live and study this exciting planet and the others beyond it.

Asteroids   Thousands of tiny planets are found in orbit between Mars and Jupiter. Ceres, the largest, is only about 600 mi (960 km) in diameter. Most are far smaller than that. Most of the asteroids are not spherical-shaped. Scientists think they are material left over when the solar system formed about 4.6 billion years ago, but just never pulled together to form a single planet. Sometimes, the asteroids stray closer to Earth and are pulled in by the gravity. They are called meteors. There is a crater in Arizona that is 4,100 feet (1,366 m) wide and 600 feet (200 m) deep caused by a large asteroid that struck earth.

Jupiter   This giant is the largest of the planets. More than 11 Earths could fit across its diameter. The unmanned satellites *Voyager I* and *II* flew by Jupiter in 1979, sending spectacular images back to Earth showing clouds swirling in severe storms. One cloud formation is called the Great Red Spot, which is a storm that has been raging for at least three hundred years. It could swallow two or three Earths! The planet is made up mostly of clouds of liquid hydrogen, which get extremely hot near the center. This huge planet swirls around its axis at an unbelievable speed once every ten hours. This rapid rotation and the heat of the atmosphere create the great storms that rage constantly on Jupiter. A year on Jupiter is equal to almost 12 earth years. *Voyager* discovered a thin ring around Jupiter, almost like a moon that got too close and was pulled apart by the strong gravity of this remarkable planet. Jupiter has at least 16 moons, four of which were discovered by Galileo. The moon Io is nearest the planet and is constantly being turned "inside out" by the gravitational pull of Jupiter. Images from *Voyager* showed volcanoes erupting on Io's surface, the only other place besides Earth where this has been seen.

Just the Facts *(cont.)*

Saturn

This enormous planet has excited scientists and amateur astronomers since its swirling rings were first discovered. Galileo was the first to see the rings, but his telescope was not good enough to show them clearly. He wrote that "Saturn has ears." The rings were clearly seen some years later by another astronomer. Although all four giant planets have rings, Saturn's is the largest system. Various-sized chunks of rock and ice orbit around the equator of this huge planet like many super highways. Scientists believe they are most likely material that never formed into moons. Saturn has about 20 moons, one of which travels in the opposite direction around it than all the others. Titan is the largest moon and even has an atmosphere. Like Jupiter, Saturn rotates in ten hours and takes about 29 1/2 earth years to orbit the sun. Its atmosphere is also like Jupiter's, mostly liquid hydrogen and constantly stormy.

Uranus

Uranus is the planet that scientists say "got knocked on its side." It has a thin ring system orbiting its equator, which is tilted since the poles point toward the sun. Although not as large as Jupiter or Saturn, four Earths could fit across its diameter. A day on Uranus is about 17 hours long. One trip around the sun on Uranus takes 84 years. This planet is so far from the sun that it was not discovered until 1781. It has 15 moons, ten of which were discovered by *Voyager* as it flew by Uranus in 1986.

Neptune

Voyager flew by this planet as it did Jupiter, Saturn, and Uranus, sending back spectacular images of a pale blue planet. The blue was not from water on the surface, but from clouds of hydrogen and helium. This planet is 30 times farther from the sun than Earth. Its year is equal to 165 Earth years. Due to its distance, it was not discovered until 1841. Scientists predicted Neptune would have rings like the other three giant planets. This was confirmed when *Voyager* images showed thin rings. This planet is nearly a twin in size to Uranus as well as in the length of its day, which is about 18 hours long. Like Jupiter, Neptune has a hurricane raging in its atmosphere that forms a huge dark spot. Winds gust to 1,200 mph (1,920 kmph) on this planet, the fastest in the solar system. If you lived on Neptune, you would have a birthday only once every 165 years! There are eight moons orbiting this planet. Triton, the largest moon, has geysers spewing invisible nitrogen gas 500 mi (800 km) into space.

Just the Facts *(cont.)*

Pluto   Appropriately named for the god of the underworld, this planet is so far away from the sun that the light would appear only as a bright star. This is the smallest planet in the solar system. It is not even as large as Earth's moon, yet it has a moon of its own. This moon is called Charon and is about half as large as Pluto. Pluto was discovered in 1930 by Clyde Tombaugh, a young assistant at the Lowell Observatory in Arizona. Its orbit is very elliptical, sometimes carrying it inside Neptune's orbit. This happened in 1977, making Neptune the most distant planet in the solar system until 1999, when Pluto's orbit takes it beyond this planet.

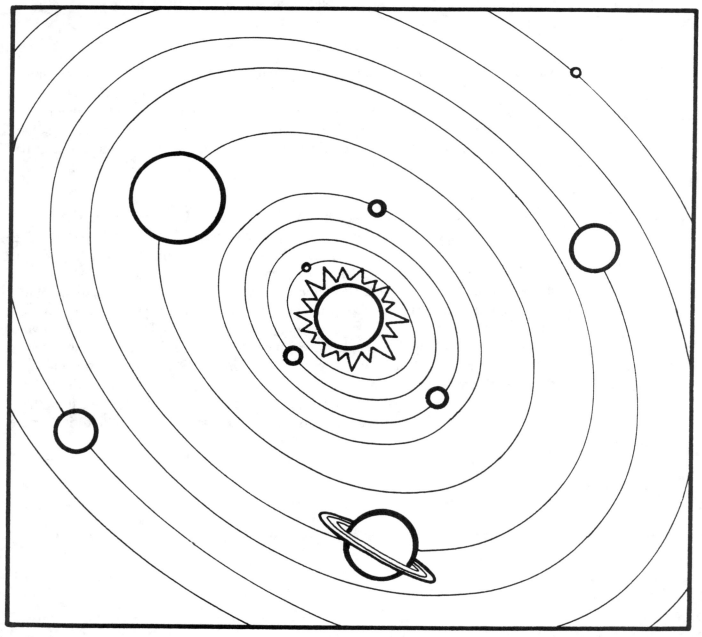

14

Our Star, the Sun

Question

What can we learn from observing the sun?

Setting the Stage

- As students arrive, let them look at the shadow record sheet you have taped on the pavement.
- Ask them what they think you are recording on the paper.
- Tell the students that people long ago watched the sun moving from one side of the earth to the other and thought some mystical power made it move.
- Explain that today we know it is the Earth's rotation around its axis that makes the sun appear to move.
- Let them know that during this lesson, they will record the motion the sun appears to make across the sky.

Materials Needed for Entire Class

- 4' (120 cm) of 36" (90 cm) white butcher paper
- ring stand or other type of stand with a stick held perpendicular to the ground
- black permanent marker
- tape measure

Teacher Preparation

On a sunny day, before school begins, tape the butcher paper to a paved area near the classroom where it will receive sun all day. Align it east–west and put the stick on its stand midway between the long ends, on the south edge. You may wish to use a compass to be sure of the direction of the paper. Tape the stand in place or draw around its base so it will always be in the same position. Write the date and directions on the paper. Use the black pen to mark the tip of the shadow on the paper with a dot, then record the time next to the dot.

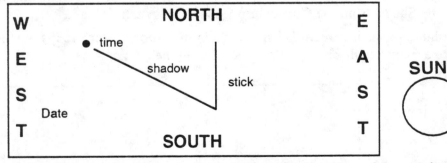

Procedure

1. While students are observing the stick's shadow, discuss the direction of the sun in the morning, noon, and evening so students will realize it appears to travel across the sky in a great arc from east to west.
2. During this discussion period, the shadow will have moved, and most students will notice this happening. They will be surprised at how fast it moves. Mark the tip of the shadow again.
3. Have students predict which direction the shadow will move in the next few minutes.

Our Star, the Sun *(cont.)*

Procedure *(cont.)*

4. Explain to students the motion of the shadow is caused by the Earth's rotation. Ask them to calculate the speed of the Earth at the equator: the Earth's circumference at the equator is about 25,000 mi (40,000 km).

   One day is 24 hours long.

   What is the speed of the Earth at the equator? 25,000 mi (40,000 kmph) = 1,042 mph (1667 kmph).

   As you move closer to the poles, the speed is less, and is 0 at the poles.

5. Ask students if they now understand why the shadow moves so fast across the paper.

6. Mark the shadow again.

7. Divide students into eight groups and have them predict where the shadow will be in 15 minutes. Give each group a number and have the students mark their number on the paper to show the spot they predicted will be at the tip of the shadow.

Extensions

- Have students return to the paper 15 minutes later to check the accuracy of the predictions.
- Assign students to continue to mark the shadow at half-hour intervals.
- Have students look at the stick's shadow just before school ends. Discuss its length and direction changes that occurred during the day.
- The shadow swept from west to east, the opposite direction of the sun's motion.
- Shadows were longest in the early morning and late afternoon.
- Measure the length of the shadow using the tape measure. Mark the shortest shadow.
- The shortest shadow was at mid-day (noon by the sun, not necessarily by the clock).

Closure

- Let students measure the angle of the sun above the horizon by conducting the lesson: "How High is the Sun?" from the Curriculum Connections section (page 72).
- Make miniature shadow records using a T pin in cardboard for groups of students to record the sun once a month to discover the changes during the year.

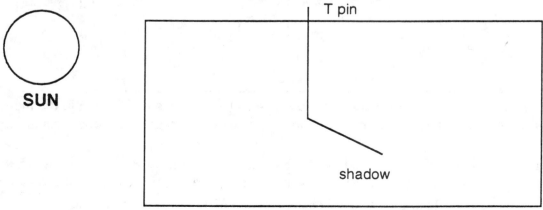

paper covered cardboard

Scale Model of the Planets

Question

How big are the planets?

Setting the Stage

Divide students into nine groups and have them use a compass to draw circles on a large sheet of construction paper to represent the nine planets, showing their size comparisons, based upon their present knowledge.

Materials Needed for Each Group

- nine sheets of large construction paper
- 6" (15 cm) square of red, gray, blue, white, and black
- two different colors 4' x 1' (120 cm x 30 cm) butcher paper
- two different colors 2' x 1' (60 cm x 30 cm) butcher paper
- ruler or meter stick
- 15 yds (m) of heavy string
- four index cards
- five compasses (for groups drawing the five small planets)
- nine calculators
- data-capture sheet (page 19), one per student

Procedure

1. Have each of the nine groups complete their data-capture sheets.
2. Assign a different planet to each of the groups and give each group the paper needed for their planet as follows:
- 6" (15 cm) squares: red (Mars), gray (Mercury), blue (Earth), white (Venus), and black (Pluto)
- two different colors 4' x 1' (120 cm x 30 cm) butcher paper (Jupiter and Saturn)
- two different colors or 2' x 1' (60 cm x 30 cm) butcher paper (Uranus and Neptune)
3. To draw Mercury, Venus, Mars, Earth, and Pluto, tell students to stretch the compass to the exact length of the radius of the planet's scale size and draw a circle in the center of the paper.
4. Groups drawing the larger planets will not be able to use the standard compass, since their circles will be too large. They will use the following technique:
- Cut a string 2" (5 cm) longer than the length needed for the radius.
- Tie a loop in the end of the string.
- Punch a hole in the center of one edge of the file card and tie the string through the hole so that when the string is stretched tight, it measures the exact radius needed.

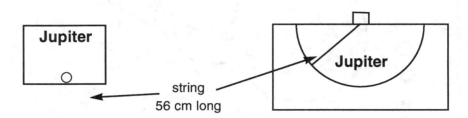

Scale Model of the Planets *(cont.)*

Procedure *(cont.)*
- Pin the paper being used for the larger planets on a bulletin board.
- The groups drawing Neptune and Uranus will place their card with its string in the center of the paper, pushing a pin into the hole with the string through it.
- The groups drawing Jupiter and Saturn will place the card in the middle of the long edge of the paper; they will draw only half a circle.

5. Each group should label the planet it drew with its name and diameter, and then superimpose the scale models as shown below:

(1) Uranus
(2) Neptune
(3) Earth
(4) Venus
(5) Mars
(6) Mercury
(7) Pluto

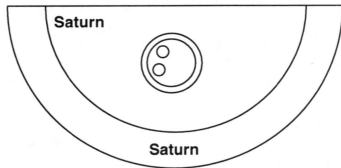

Extensions
- Have students compare the diameter of each of the other planets with that of the Earth's.
- Have students fold the earth model in half and place it along the diameter of Jupiter. Count how many "Earths" would fit across this giant planet. Repeat this, comparing Earth with all other planets. Then have them record this information on their data-capture sheets.
- Pin this scale model to the bulletin board for future use.
- Have students make a scale model of the sun's diameter with string to compare with the planets.

Closure

Make a copy of the Solar System Statistics information for each student to place in their space journal.

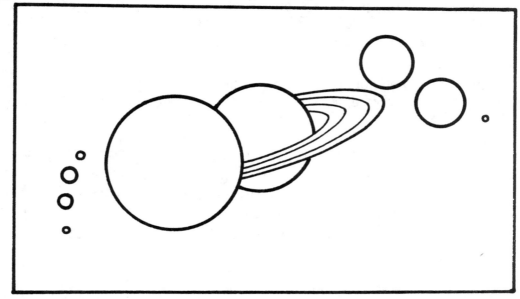

Scale Model of the Planets *(cont.)*

Make a scale model of the solar system by drawing circles for each of the planets. The scale you will use is shown below:

Earth's radius 3,964 mi (6,342 km) = 2" (5 cm)

The diameters of the planets, relative to that of Earth's, are listed on the chart below. Finish the calculations to find the size of the scale model. Round off the radius of each model to the nearest tenth (e.g., 6.75 becomes 6.8 and 6.74 becomes 6.7). Stretch your compass or string to the length of the radius and draw a circle that represents each of the planets and Earth's Moon.

Planet	Diameter Relative to Earth's	Radius of Model
Mercury	.38 x 2" (5 cm)	
Venus	.95 x 2" (5 cm)	
Earth	1.00 x 2" (5 cm)	
Mars	.53 x 2" (5 cm)	
Jupiter	10.79 x 2" (5 cm)	
Saturn	8.91 x 2" (5 cm)	
Uranus	4.05 x 2" (5 cm)	
Neptune	3.91 x 2" (5 cm)	
Pluto	.8 x 2" (5 cm)	
Earth's Moon	.27 x 2" (5 cm)	

Scale Model of the Sun

The sun is an average-sized star, but it is still 109 times larger than Earth. It would not be possible to make a paper model of it, since this would not fit into your classroom. Use string to make a model of the diameter of the sun as follows:

The Sun's diameter = 109 x 4" (10 cm) Earth's diameter to scale = _____ in (cm) in diameter
Convert this diameter to meters:
_____ in (cm) in diameter ÷ 100 = _____ yds (m) in diameter

Measure a string that equals the scaled-down diameter of the sun, and then compare it to the planets. You will need to do this outside your classroom.

Use the scale model of the planets your class has made to help you complete the following information:

How many Earths would fit across the diameter of the giant planets?
    Jupiter = _____   Saturn = _____   Uranus = _____   Neptune = _____
The Earth is about _____ times larger than the Moon and _____ times larger than Mars.
The Earth is nearly the same size as the planet _____.
What other planets are nearly twins? _____ and _____.

How Much Do You Weigh?

Question

How much would you weigh on other planets in our solar system and on the moon?

Setting the Stage

- Review with students the sizes of the planets that were made to scale in the lesson, Scale Model of the Planets.

- Explain to students the planets and the moon vary in mass as well as size and that the greater the mass, the more gravitational pull. This means you weigh more on a planet or moon having more mass than the Earth and less on those having less mass than Earth.

Materials Needed for Each Individual

- scale models of the planets from the activity, Scale Model of the Planets
- calculators
- data-capture sheets (pages 21-22)

Procedure

1. Have students use their calculators to complete their data-capture sheets (pages 21-22).
2. Have each student graph the results to show their weight on the various planets and the moon.

Extensions

- Have them write and illustrate a story describing what it would feel like to walk on the moon, since they would weigh only about 1/6 their weight on Earth.
- Have students record the mass information on the scale models of the planets.

Closure

Have students place their finished data-capture sheets in their space journals.

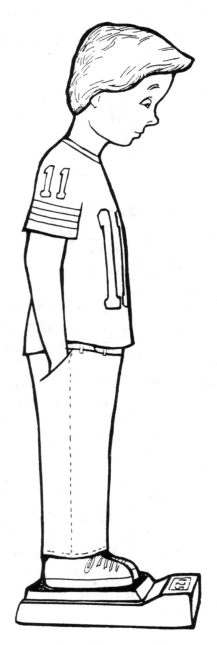

20

How Much Do You Weigh? (cont.)

How much do you weigh? Your weight depends upon where you are. If you are in orbit around the Earth, far away from Earth's gravitational pull, you would be weightless and would float. Mass is the amount of matter that makes up an object. The gravitational pull depends upon mass. Even a pencil has mass. Thus, it has a gravitational pull, but since it is far less than the Earth's mass, it falls to the ground when you drop it.

If you were to visit planets and moons with more or less mass than Earth's, a scale would show you weighed a different amount than you do on Earth. Complete the chart to find out how much you would weigh on the planets in our solar system and on the Moon.

Planet	Surface Gravity	Your Weight on Earth	New Weight
Mercury	.38 x		
Venus	.90 x		
Earth	1.00 x		
Mars	.38 x		
Jupiter	2.64 x		
Saturn	1.13 x		
Uranus	.89 x		
Neptune	1.13 x		
Pluto	.06 x		
Earth's Moon	.17 x		

How Much Do You Weigh? (cont.)

Make a graph to show the results of your calculations from your data-capture sheet (page 21).

MY WEIGHT ON THE PLANETS AND THE MOON

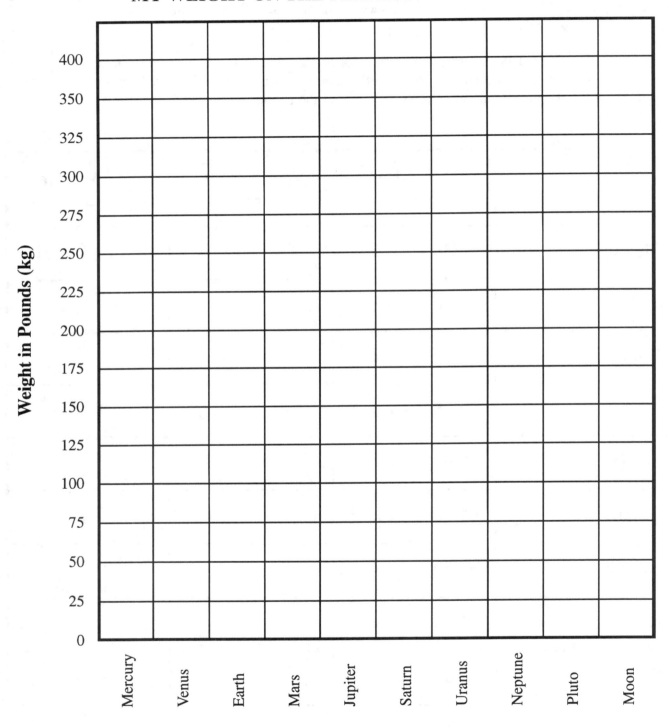

Scale Model of the Solar System

Question

How large is our solar system?

Setting the Stage

- Review with students the activity of creating a scale model of the planets and remind them of the scale that was used—Earth's diameter of 7,927 mi (12,683 km) = 4" (10 cm).

- Tell students they are going to construct a scale model of the solar system using a very different scale.

- Tell students the distance from Earth to the sun—93,000,000 mi (1,490,000,000 km)—is called one astronomical unit (1 AU). On the scale used here, it equals 1 yd (1 m).

- Tell students the distances for the remaining planets will be computed on the basis of that of Earth's.

- Tell students they will complete a data-capture sheet (page 25) to find the scale distances between the planets.

Materials Needed for Each Group

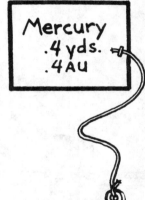

- at least 300' (100 m) of heavy string

- six pieces of heavy cardboard approximately 5" x 8" (12.5 cm x 20 cm)

- three pieces of heavy cardboard approximately 8" x 10" (20 cm x 25 cm)

- nine metal washers to tie on the end of the string to keep it from fraying

- nine yard or meter sticks

- data-capture sheet (page 25), one per student

Procedure

1. Divide students into nine groups and have each group complete their data-capture sheets.

2. Assign each of the groups to a different planet and have students prepare a piece of heavy cardboard by labeling it with their planet's name and distance from the sun in yds (m) and astronomical units. Give the larger cardboard to the groups doing Uranus, Neptune, and Pluto.

3. Monitor their work to be certain they all derive the correct answers for the distances.

4. Have each group cut a length of string equal to their planet's scale distance, and then tie a washer on the end of the string and staple the other end to the cardboard.

5. The students doing planets more distant than Mars will need to tape their yard (meter) stick to a table and keep careful count of the yds (m) of string as they measure. One of the group's members should wind the string on the cardboard as another measures it to avoid it becoming tangled.

Scale Model of the Solar System *(cont.)*

Extensions

- Have students lay their strings down, along with the picture of their planets.

- Have students take a "walk" through the solar system, having a spokesperson from each of the nine groups provide some interesting information about the group's planet.

- Explain to students all the planets travel around the sun in the same direction, but do not move in a straight path, since the closer they are to the sun, the faster they move.

- Take students to a large area to stretch out their strings, and use nine people to represent the sun. Have them stand in a circle with their backs to each other. They each hold the end of one of the nine planets. When the string is stretched out, the planets will be spread around the "sun."

Closure

In their space journals, have students draw a picture of their class's solar system.

Scale Model of the Solar System *(cont.)*

Complete the chart to find the length of string needed to form the Model of the Solar System. The scale for this model is shown below:

Earth's average distance from the sun 93,000,000 mi (1,490,000,000 km) = 1 yd (1 m)

This distance between the Earth and sun is often referred to as one astronomical unit (1 AU) and is used in the data on this chart.

PLANET	DISTANCE FROM SUN	SCALE	LENGTH OF STRING
Mercury	0.4 AU	x 1 yd (1 m)	_____ yds (m)
Venus	0.7 AU	x 1 yd (1 m)	_____ yds (m)
Earth	1.0 AU	x 1 yd (1 m)	_____ yds (m)
Mars	1.5 AU	x 1 yd (1 m)	_____ yds (m)
Jupiter	5.2 AU	x 1 yd (1 m)	_____ yds (m)
Saturn	9.5 AU	x 1 yd (1 m)	_____ yds (m)
Uranus	19.2 AU	x 1 yd (1 m)	_____ yds (m)
Neptune	30.1 AU	x l yd (1 m)	_____ yds (m)
Pluto	39.4 AU	x 1 yd (1 m)	_____ yds (m)

Which planet was assigned to your group? _____

What is the length of string you will need for this planet for the scale model? _____ yds (m).

List some interesting information about this planet that you will share with your class:

_____

_____

_____

_____

_____

Just the Facts

The history of space travel really began over 300 years ago, in the early 1600s, when Johannes Kepler, a German scientist, described the way planets in the solar system move around the sun. His description is still used today to plot the orbits of anything launched into space from Earth.

Sir Isaac Newton, an English scientist, published his Laws of Motion, based on Kepler's work. These laws are used to plan today's space flights. The way a rocket works is based upon Newton's third law: For every action, there is an equal and opposite reaction.

Konstantin Tsiolkovsky, a Russian teacher, published the first scientific paper on the use of rockets for space travel in 1903, but very few people paid attention to his ideas. Robert Goddard, an American, and Hermann Oberth, of Germany, are called "the fathers of space flight." Working separately, each of them wrote how rockets could be launched into space.

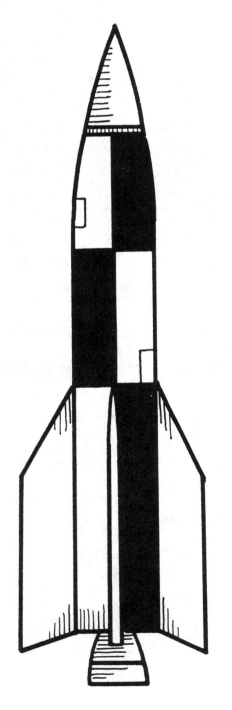

Robert Goddard built and launched the first successful liquid fuel rocket in 1926. His first rocket was small enough to be carried by a few people to its launch site on a friend's farm. It did not go into orbit around the Earth, but reached an altitude of 41' (13 m) in 2 1/2 seconds. It proved that liquid propellant could be used to launch rockets.

In the early 1940s, during World War II, German scientists developed the V-2 guided missile. It was capable of traveling from Germany to England faster than the speed of sound, but could not go fast enough to orbit the Earth. Following the war, many German scientists who had helped build this rocket fled to America or the Soviet Union and continued building rockets for these nations.

The Soviet Union had the advantage over the Americans at first. Their rockets were more powerful and could carry more weight into space. They succeeded in launching the first piece of hardware into Earth's orbit, an unmanned satellite named *Sputnik I*, which circled our planet for 22 days in 1957. The USSR had many other "firsts" in space, including orbiting the first man (and woman), but they never succeeded in sending humans out of the Earth's orbit. They have placed many space stations in orbit around the Earth, including *Mir* (Russian for "peace"), which is still in space today. Russians also hold the world record for the longest time humans have stayed in space. Two cosmonauts (Russian astronauts) stayed in space aboard *Mir* in 1987–1988 for 366 days.

Just the Facts *(cont.)*

Wernher von Braun, a German scientist, came to the United States and worked with a team of scientists to develop the spacecraft used in America's space program in the late 1940s. There were seven men selected to be the first astronauts for the *Mercury* missions, which took place from 1961 to 1963. The first of two launches that carried a single astronaut did not orbit the Earth, but landed in the Atlantic Ocean as planned, shortly after launch. As larger rockets were built, more weight could be lifted into orbit. The *Gemini* missions began in 1965 and carried two men in orbit around the Earth. Finally, in 1968, the huge Saturn rocket was ready for the Apollo missions. It was powerful enough to lift a three-person crew into orbit around the Earth. Then using its extra rocket sections, it could send them to the moon and return them safely to Earth. During the time from the first landing on the moon in 1969 and the last in 1972, there were six landings, each taking two men to the moon's surface. The last three *Apollo* missions also carried an electric car (lunar rover), which the astronauts drove to explore some areas of the moon. These trips returned to Earth with samples of the lunar soil and rocks, which are still being studied by scientists today.

The Great Space Race

Question

What is the historical background of manned space exploration?

Setting the Stage

- Ask students to tell who was the first person to go into space. (Most will respond that it was Neil Armstrong.)
- Have students read Just the Facts (pages 26-27).
- Explain to students this lesson will review the competition between the US and USSR as they raced to see who would be the first country to send people to the moon.

Materials Needed for Each Individual

- enlarged copy of the Space Exploration Time line from 1957 through 1972 (See pages 89-96).
- 2.75" (7 cm) roll of adding machine tape
- pictures of manned space missions (See Resources, pages 87-88).
- videotape *The Eagle Has Landed: The Flight of Apollo 11* (See Resources, pages 87-88).
- large bulletin board

Teacher Preparation

- Cut 16' (5 m) of adding machine tape and divide it into feet (30 cm). Mark each section with a different year from 1957 through 1972.
- Post this strip on a blank bulletin board to serve as the basis of a time line to show the history of space exploration during these years.
- Cut the enlarged copy of the time line data into one year sections from 1957 to 1972.

Procedure

1. Divide students into eight groups and distribute the strips of time line data to them.
2. Have each group read over the information, and then select a spokesperson.
3. Appoint two students to keep score, one for the USSR and the other for the USA. Have them record on the board successful launches for each nation as they are placed on the time line.
4. Ask each group's spokesperson to present the space history for their year, calling them in sequence and posting each information sheet on the bulletin board above the corresponding date on the time line.

Extension

Have students make drawings to place on the Great Space Race bulletin board to depict the events that happened each year.

Closure

Have students continue adding to their time lines, placing additional space travel events throughout this study.

Race to the Moon

Question

Who won the race to the moon?

Setting the Stage

- Display for students The Great Space Race time line on a bulletin board.
- Explain to students this lesson will require that each student use the information on this time line to complete his or her data-capture sheet (page 31) over the next few days.

Teacher Materials

- copy of answers to data-capture sheet (page 30)

Materials Needed for Each Individual

- copy of data-capture sheet (page 31)

Procedure

1. Distribute to students a copy of the data-capture sheet.
2. Let students consult The Great Space Race time line on bulletin board to complete their answers.

Extensions

- Have students use other resources to fill in some interesting additional information about the space events of this time.
- Have students find other events that were going on in the world during these same years and add them to the time line.

Closure

Have students cut the information placed on their data-capture sheets into strips and paste them in order on another paper. They should put the title, Race to the Moon, on that paper, and then write information about the first moon landing on the paper and add them to their space journals.

Race to the Moon (cont.)

Answers to student data-capture sheet.

GOALS	DATE	NATION	SPACECRAFT
First satellite to orbit Earth	1957	USSR	*Sputnik I*
Send a live animal into space	1957	USSR	*Sputnik II*
Send an object out of Earth's orbit	1959	USSR	*Luna 1*
Send an object to surface of moon	1959	USSR	*Luna 2*
Photograph moon	1959	USSR	*Luna 3*
Recover live animal from orbit	1960	USSR	*Sputnik V*
Send a human into space	1961	USSR	*Vostok l*
First dual mission	1963	USSR	*Vostok 5-6*
Send three people into space	1964	USSR	*Voshkod I*
Walk outside spacecraft while in orbit	1965	USSR	*Voshkod 11*
Dock with another spacecraft while in orbit	1965	USA	*Gemini 6-7*
Soft land an object on the moon	1966	USSR	*Luna 9*
Move to orbit 850 miles (1,360 km) above Earth	1966	USA	*Gemini 11*
Stay in orbit for over 100 orbits	1968	USA	*Apollo 7*
First to fly around moon and return to Earth	1968	USSR	*Zond 5*
First humans to orbit moon	1968	USA	*Apollo 8*
First test of lunar module in lunar orbit	1969	USA	*Apollo 10*
First manned lunar landing	1969	USA	*Apollo 11*

Race to the Moon *(cont.)*

The Soviet Union (USSR) and the United States (US) were involved in a race to see which nation would reach the moon first. This contest began in 1957. Use information from The Great Space Race time line to fill in the following information. The first one is done for you as an example.

GOALS	DATE	NATION	SPACECRAFT
First satellite to orbit Earth	1957	USSR	*Sputnik I*
First dual mission			
Send an object to surface of moon			
Walk outside spacecraft while in orbit			
Stay in orbit for over 100 orbits			
Send a live animal into space			
First test of lunar module in lunar orbit			
Photograph moon			
Send three people into space			
Recover live animal from orbit			
Send an object out of Earth's orbit			
First manned *lunar* landing			
Send a human into space			
Dock with another spacecraft in orbit			
Soft land an object on the moon			
First to fly around moon and return to Earth			
Move to orbit 850 miles (1,360 km) above Earth			
First humans to orbit moon			

These events are not listed in order. Now that you know the dates when they occurred, cut the information into strips and paste them in order on another piece of paper. Write the title *Race to the Moon* on the paper. Find out information about the first landing on the moon and write a paragraph about it.

#639 Space—Intermediate

3...2...1...Liftoff!

Question
What does it take to launch something into space?

Setting the Stage
- Explain to students a rocket needs to travel at a speed of 17,500 mph (28,000 kmph) to stay in orbit around Earth. Satellites or space vehicles sent beyond the Earth must travel at about 25,000 mph (40,000 kmph) to escape the pull of gravity.
- Tell students this requires a great deal of thrust (push), and, therefore, fuel, to lift something off the Earth and place it in orbit.
- Tell students this activity will show them what it is like to launch something into space.

Materials Needed for Each Group
- tennis ball marked with a number on each ball
- materials to use to construct a launcher (e.g., rubber bands, springs, poles, etc.)
- data-capture sheet (page 34), one per student

Teacher Preparation
Mark off a large field (preferably a grass area) with seven lengths of string placed 5' (1.5 m) apart covering an area of 35' (12 m). Each length of string should be at least 25' (8 m) long.

Procedure
1. Take students to the field and divide them into pairs.
2. Give each pair a numbered tennis ball.
3. One partner from each pair stands along the first string, separated at arm's length from the next person.
4. Have the other members of the pairs stand on the second string facing their partners, who are 5' (1.5 m) from them.
5. Tell the partner on the inside line to hold the ball and be ready to drop it when you give a signal. After the ball is dropped, discuss why it dropped to the ground. (The gravity of Earth pulls it toward its center.)
6. Ask students to throw the ball to their partners so it will land just in front of them. Then have them describe what they did to make it travel that distance. Ask if the ball fell back to Earth.
7. Have one partner stay on the first line, while the other goes to the third line, 15' away. Tell students to toss the ball so it lands near their partners' feet. Discuss with students what had to change to get the ball to travel this far. (It had to be tossed with greater force.)
8. Begin with the same partner standing on line one while the other partner stands on line seven. Challenge the partners on line one to toss the balls as far as they can. When their partners see where the balls bounce, they go stand on that spot.
9. Ask students to describe the amount of energy needed to throw the ball to this distance as compared to the 5' (1.5 m) and 10' (3 m) throw.

3...2...1...Liftoff! *(cont.)*

Extensions

- Have students change places and see how far they can throw the ball.
- Ask students what they would have to do to send their balls into space; be sure they understand that they would need a great deal more energy than a person can provide.

Closure

Divide students into eight groups and have them construct a tennis ball launcher. Have them complete their data-capture sheets and add them to their space journals.

3...2...1...Liftoff! *(cont.)*

You are a space engineer who has been asked to design a launching device to send a tennis ball into orbit around the Earth. Draw a picture of the launcher you will build using materials that are available to you. These may include such items as rubber bands, a baseball bat, springs, and any other things that may help you send your tennis ball as far as possible.

Draw your tennis ball launcher. Be sure to label all the materials you will use to make it.

After building your tennis ball launcher, take it to the field that is marked off with string at 5' (1.5 m) intervals. Set your launcher on the first string and launch your ball, recording its distance after each of three trials. Remodel the launcher to improve it and repeat the three trials. Show what changes you made by making another drawing or adding to the one above.

TESTING THE TENNIS BALL LAUNCHER

Original Launcher		Remodeled Launcher	
Trial #	Number of Feet (m)	Trial #	Number of Feet (m)
1	_____	1	_____
2	_____	2	_____
3	_____	3	_____

Early Space Vehicles

Question

How large were the early American and Russian space vehicles?

Setting the Stage

- Tell students that most of the first space vehicles were mounted on top of rockets that were meant to be used in war. Later, rockets were developed to lift space vehicles into orbit around the Earth.

- Explain to students these rockets had to be huge and very powerful in order to reach the speed necessary to orbit the Earth. Space capsules were mounted on these rockets. At first, they could only carry one passenger, but as they became more powerful, they lifted up to three passengers. The space capsules were very tiny in comparison to the rockets and were the only part to return to Earth with the astronauts or cosmonauts.

- Tell students that in this lesson, they will find out how large these rockets became during the years of the Great Space Race.

Materials Needed for Entire Class

- strings that represent the lengths of the space rockets used in the *Mercury, Gemini,* and *Apollo* missions

- pictures of the rockets from these missions (See Resources, pages 87–88.)

- data-capture sheet (page 37), one per student

Teacher Preparation

Cut lengths of heavy string for the space rockets listed below and mount them on heavy cardboard.

American and Russian Space Vehicles

Name	Years	Length	Missions
Vostok	1957–1964	125' (42 m)	USSR launched *Sputnik* and cosmonauts.
	1961		First man in space Yuri Gargarin.
Mercury	1962–1963	87' (29 m)	American, could carry only one astronaut at a time.
	1962		John Glenn makes 3 orbits.
Gemini	1965–1967	160' (53 m)	American, could carry two astronauts. Practiced meeting in space while orbiting Earth.
Soyuz	1967–(?)	167' (56 m)	USSR manned launches capable of carrying two cosmonauts.
Apollo (Saturn V rocket)	1967–1975	363' (121 m)	American moon missions, capsule mounted on huge three-stage Saturn rocket.
	July 20, 1969		First landing on the moon.

Early Space Vehicles *(cont.)*

Procedure

1. Take students to a large field to stretch out the strings for each of the five space rockets.

2. Select ten students to work in pairs and have them stand face to face at one end of the field.

3. Distribute a card with the string on it to each pair, in order of the years as shown on the chart.

4. Stretch the strings out across an open field in the order shown in the chart, beginning with *Vostok.*

5. Students will be impressed by the enormous size of the *Apollo*/Saturn V. Let them walk its length and be sure they know that this rocket took off standing upright, not lying on its side.

Extensions

- Divide students into groups and have them complete their data-capture sheets.

- Have students research additional information regarding these space missions (See Resources and bibliography, pages 85-88). Have groups of students create a mock TV quiz show using the historical information they glean in their research. Add the history to the time line.

Closure

Show students videos of the *Apollo 11* through *17* missions.

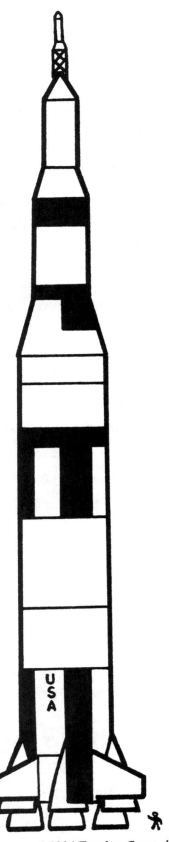

36

Early Space Vehicles *(cont.)*

You are a team of rocket engineers who must do the following:

- Construct a rocket engine using one to three balloons.

- Make a rocket from a cardboard tube and mount it on your rocket.

- Set up a launch site using the string 3 yds (3 m) in length.

- Complete the rest of the information required, and then launch your rocket and record your data.

Materials Needed for Each Group

- three strong, long balloons
- 3 yds (3 m) of string
- 1-2 drinking straws
- transparent tape
- cardboard tube

ROCKET STATISTICS

Weight _____ oz (g)   Length _____ in (cm)

DRAWING OF THE ROCKET

LAUNCH TESTS

HORIZONTAL →	VERTICAL ↑
Trial # 1 _____ in (cm)	Trial # 1 _____ in (cm)
Trial # 2 _____ in (cm)	Trial # 2 _____ in (cm)
Trial # 3 _____ in (cm)	Trial # 3 _____ in (cm)
Trial # 4 _____ in (cm)	Trial # 4 _____ in (cm)

Just the Facts

Skylab

The American space station *Skylab* was launched into orbit around the Earth in 1973. It was constructed inside a second stage of the three-stage Saturn rocket, which had been designed to take the Apollo astronauts to the moon. During launch, a solar panel and the meteoroid shield were torn off. The first crew of astronauts to reach *Skylab* several days later fastened an umbrella made of thin reflective plastic to the side in place of the shield, so the sun would not overheat the space station. They also released a solar panel that had not opened as it was designed to do. This took several hours of hard work in spacesuits outside the space station.

Skylab was visited by three three-man crews during 1973. The longest stay was 84 days. These astronauts did a great deal of scientific research while orbiting the Earth. They had a telescope with which they observed and photographed the sun. Many photographs of Earth were also taken that showed views of land formations, ocean currents, and atmosphere. They also conducted experiments on themselves to find out how the human body is affected by life in microgravity.

The Earth's atmosphere is constantly being bombarded by energy from the sun, including magnetic radiation. About every 11 years, there is an increase in magnetic storms on the sun, causing large sunspots and solar prominences to appear in the upper layers of the sun. This results in an expansion of the Earth's atmosphere, and creates a drag on anything orbiting the planet at lower levels. This phenomenon occurred in 1979, and since there was no way to pull *Skylab* into a higher orbit, it began to slow down as it rubbed against the atmosphere. Scientists could calculate when it would fall to Earth and knew most of it would be burned up by the friction of the atmosphere during reentry. Finally, in July, 1979, *Skylab* began to fall to Earth. As it came closer, the small jets on Skylab were fired and started it tumbling. This caused most of the sections that made it through the atmosphere to fall into the ocean. People in Perth, Australia, saw a spectacular fiery display that night as the 77-ton (69-tonn) space station broke apart and burned in the Earth's atmosphere. The biggest sections came down in a sparsely populated region several hundred miles (km) east of Perth. One of these pieces is on display in the space museum in Huntsville, Alabama.

SPACE SHUTTLE

The space shuttle program began with the launch of *Columbia* in 1981. It was the first reusable space ship and is only launched in Florida from Kennedy Space Center, using rockets which fall away after launching it into orbit. It returns to earth like a glider, landing in California or Florida. The space shuttle can carry a crew of up to eight and has living quarters on board so the crew can stay in orbit for more than a week. The shuttle can also carry satellites or a space lab inside its huge cargo bay, which is large enough to hold a railroad boxcar. The space shuttle cannot travel to the moon, but someday it may carry parts into Earth's orbit to be used to construct a space station.

Just the Facts *(cont.)*

The space shuttles are built in California. Six have been constructed thus far:

Enterprise—This prototype, constructed just for test purposes, had no engines or insulation for space travel, since it was not intended to orbit the Earth. It was flown in tests at Edwards Air Force Base in California. There are plans to display it near Washington, DC in the future.

Columbia—The first shuttle to be launched into space on April 12, 1991, carried two astronauts, Commander John Young (who had also been to the moon) and Pilot Robert Crippen. It orbited the Earth 36 times before landing at Edwards Air Force Base, California.

Challenger—This shuttle carried the first American woman astronaut Sally Ride into space in 1983. It was destroyed when one of the solid rocket boosters exploded 73 seconds after launch on January 28, 1986, killing all seven crew members, including the first "Teacher in Space," Christa McAuliffe.

Discovery—First launched in 1984, it carried Senator Jake Garn, along with five other astronauts, into orbit in 1985. The crew of this mission conducted demonstrations for children on Earth to show how 12 toys, such as a Slinky, paper airplane, and yo-yo, reacted in the microgravity of the orbiting shuttle. On September 29, 1988, the Discovery was launched, sending Americans astronauts back into space following the Challenger disaster.

Atlantis—added to the fleet of shuttles in 1985.

Endeavor—A contest was conducted to select a name for the last shuttle. The winners were students at an elementary school. *Endeavor* was first launched June, 1993.

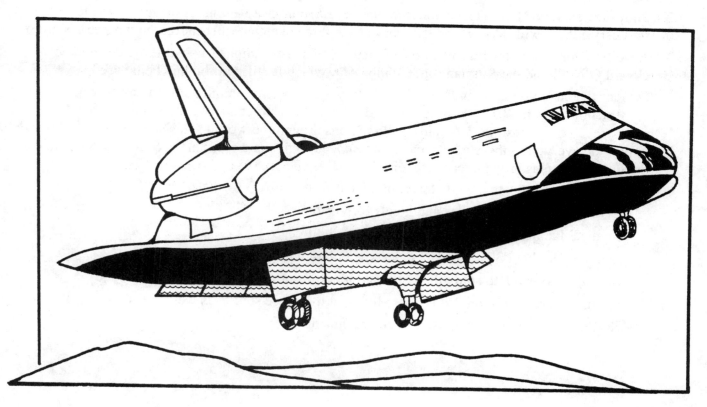

Space Stations

Question

What is a space station like?

Setting the Stage

- Review with students the information on the Space Exploration Time Line for 1971, which reports that the first space station was the Soviet *Salyut 1*. It was used by cosmonauts, but fell back to Earth in 1971; no one was aboard. The Soviets continued to launch other space stations.
- Have students add information to the Space Exploration Time Line for 1973–1980 to introduce information about space stations: America's *Skylab* and Russia's *Salyuts*.
- Tell students they are going to construct a future space station that will orbit Earth.

Materials Needed for Each Group

- diagram of *Skylab* (page 42), one per student
- variety of materials to build space station (e.g., styrofoam packaging, boxes, balls, etc.)
- glue
- paper clips
- tape

Procedure

1. Distribute copies of the *Skylab* diagram and discuss its components. Tell students that it could accommodate a three-person crew.
2. Show students the NASA videotape *3 Rooms, Earthview* (See Resources, pages 87-88) to familiarize them with Skylab and the work of the three teams of astronauts who worked aboard it.
3. Have students search for information and pictures of space stations, such as those designed by Gerard O'Neill and the Russian space station *Mir*, which is still in orbit and being used.
4. Divide students into teams and tell them: You are members of an international space station construction team in 2010. Your task is to design and construct a space station that orbits Earth and is capable of housing 25 families from nations around the world. This space station will need to provide everything these adults and children need to live and work in space for years. Include the following areas in your space station:
   - Docking ports for transports traveling to and from Earth
   - Living quarters for families and hotels for visitors
   - Medical facilities to take care of adults and children
   - Schools for about 30 students, grades kindergarten through high school
   - Scientific research to study the Earth and moon from space
   - Farms for growing food for all those living at the space station as well as visitors
   - Recreation to provide exercise and entertainment

Space Stations *(cont.)*

Extensions

- Have students write to NASA to request information regarding the proposed American space station.
- Arrange for a guest speaker who can tell students about the future space station program.
- Have students use a computer program that simulates the construction of a space station.

Closure

Have students display and explain their space stations for other classes and during an open house for parents and other visitors.

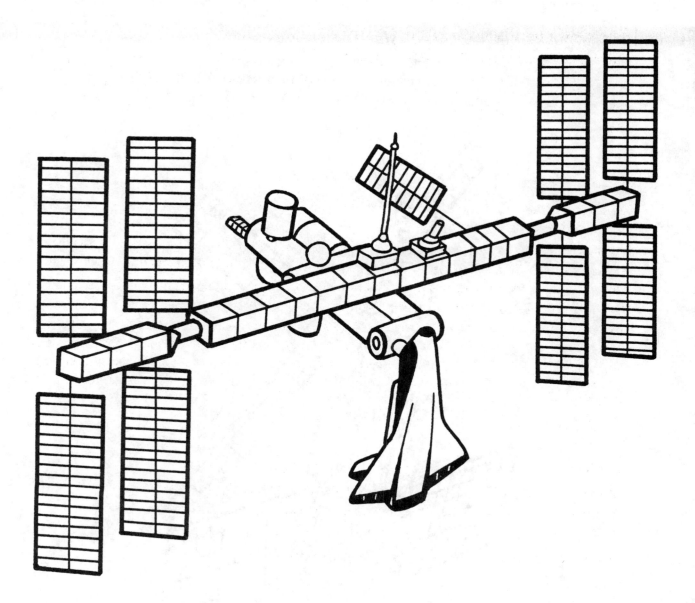

Space Stations *(cont.)*

SKYLAB

Three crews of astronauts traveled from Kennedy Space Center, Florida, to *Skylab* in 1973 aboard an *Apollo* spacecraft, splashing down in the Atlantic Ocean when they returned. This American space station was as large as a small house. It was divided into two stories: one was a science laboratory, and the other held the crew quarters, dining area, a toilet, and even a shower. Each astronaut had his own sleeping area with a sleeping bag stretched between the ceiling and floor. The astronauts could move from one part of *Skylab* to another by floating in the microgravity environment of space. They had to exercise to keep physically fit, since bones and heart are affected by lack of gravity during long stays in space. They even used the inside circular walls as a running track, which meant they ran on the floors and ceiling.

Skylab Dimensions

Length = 119 feet (36 meters)
Diameter = 27 feet (8 meters)
Interior = 12,000 cubic feet (330 cubic meters)

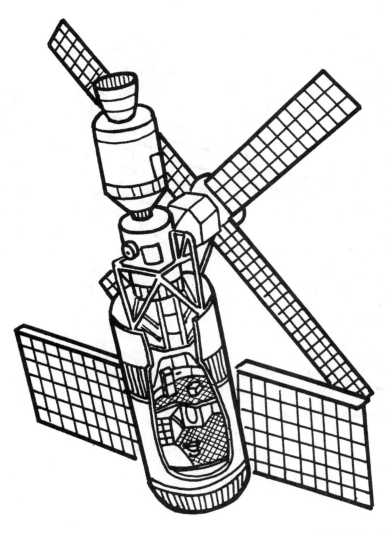

Space Shuttle

Question

How large is the space shuttle?

Setting the Stage

- Have students add the final information to the Space Exploration Time Line from 1981-1988 showing the space shuttle missions.
- Have students use the string length for the *Apollo*/Saturn V, which was made in the lesson Early Space Vehicles to compare it with a string that is 184' long (56 m) representing the length of the space shuttle including the large fuel tank.
- Explain to students the space shuttle appears shorter than the *Apollo*/Saturn V, but the difference is that the rockets are mounted on the sides of the shuttle and the Saturn V rockets were stacked one on top of the other. The Saturn V rockets also had to be larger, since they needed to boost the *Apollo* spacecraft into orbit around the Earth, and then off to the moon.

Materials Needed for Each Group

- copy of How Big Is the Space Shuttle (page 46), one per student
- data-capture sheet (page 47), one per student

Materials Needed for Entire Class

- transparencies of Cutaway Views of the Space Shuttle (pages 44-45)
- strings cut to the dimensions of the mid-deck section: Front: 8.9' (2.7 m) Sides: 13.1' (4.0 m) Back: 12' (3.7 m)

Procedure

1. Divide students into groups and distribute copies of data-capture sheets (page 47) to each group.
2. Have students discuss the parts of the shuttle once they complete the activity sheet.
3. Show students the transparencies of the Cutaway Views of the Space Shuttle (pages 44-45) to students.
4. Have students hold the strings that represent the dimensions of the mid-deck, so they will fit into the center of the classroom.
5. Show students the transparency of the mid-deck section and explain that these are the outside walls and that this area is really much smaller, since the equipment, bunks, galley, storage lockers, airlock, and toilet take up space. Also point out that this area is about 6' (2 m) high and that people can float, so they can also use the ceiling space.

Extension

Have students lay out the dimensions of the space shuttle on the playground using the dimensions shown on their data-capture sheet.

Closure

Show students a NASA video of a space shuttle mission, such as the 1984 *Challenger* mission 41-C, the launch of the long duration exposure facility (LDEF) that carried numerous science experiments into space, including tomato seeds that were later distributed to schools throughout the nation to grow.

Space Shuttle *(cont.)*

CUTAWAY VIEW OF THE SPACE SHUTTLE
FLIGHT DECK

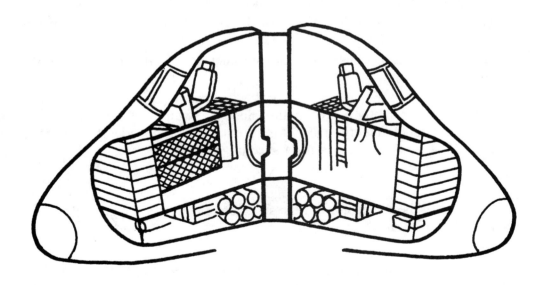

Space Shuttle (cont.)

CUTAWAY VIEW OF THE SPACE SHUTTLE
FLIGHT-DECK SEATING
MID DECK

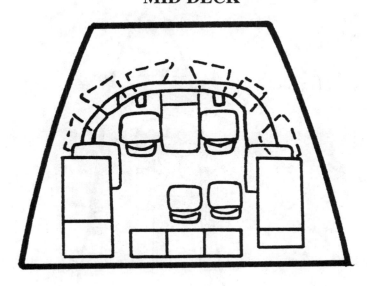

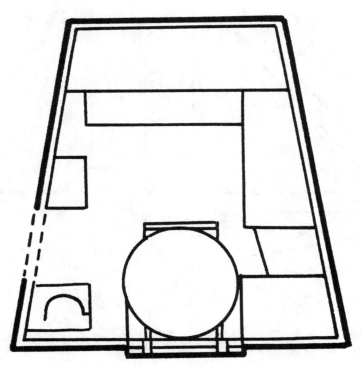

Space Shuttle *(cont.)*

HOW BIG IS THE SPACE SHUTTLE?

The dimensions of the space shuttle are shown below. Use these to lay out the shuttle on the playground or a field.

- Length = 122' (37 m)
- Body Width = 23' (7 m)
- Wingspan = 78' (24 m)
- Cargo Bay Length = 60' (18 m)

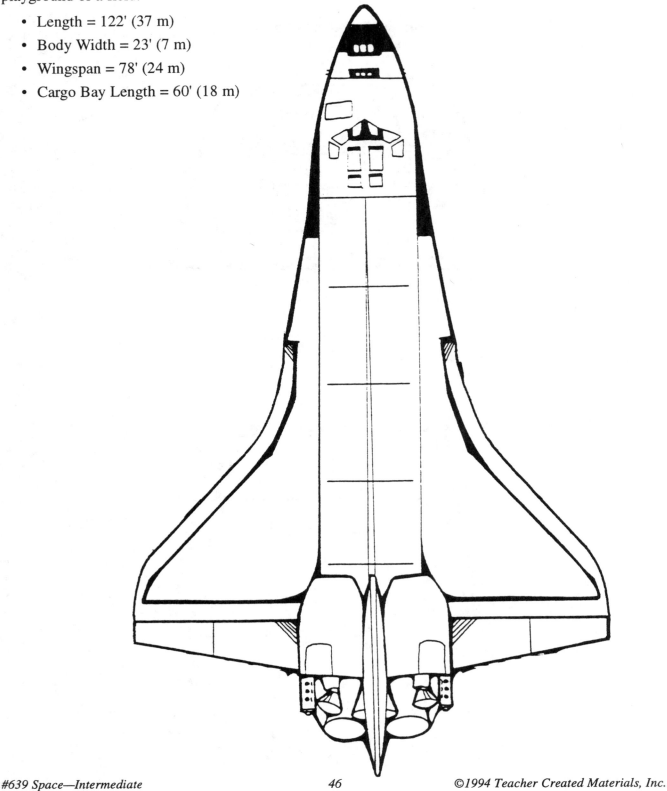

Space Shuttle *(cont.)*

Look at the views of the space shuttle, and then read the information shown below. Match the description of the parts of the shuttle by writing the number on the line that points to that part.

1. Orbiter—This looks like a large glider airplane with wings and tail. It can carry a crew of eight. While in orbit, it is usually 150–200 mi (240–320 km) above the Earth, not far enough away to see the whole planet. It circles the Earth once every 90 minutes at a speed of about 17,500 mph (28,000 kmph).

2. Space Shuttle Main Engines (SSMEs)—These are three huge engines on the tail of the Orbiter. They get their fuel from the External Tank and are used only during lift-off. When returning to Earth, the Orbiter cannot use its engines, but glides to a landing.

3. External Tank (ET)—The Orbiter is mounted on top of this huge tank, which stores the fuel for the main engines. When the fuel (propellant) is used up about eight minutes after lift-off, the external tank comes off. It burns up as it falls through the atmosphere. In the earlier flights, it was painted, but since paint adds weight and the tank is not being reused, it is no longer painted.

4. Solid Rocket Boosters (SRBs)—There are two of these rockets, one on each side of the shuttle. During launch, they are ignited just after the main engines. Once they start, they cannot be shut off, and the shuttle is lifted off the launch pad. They fall away shortly after lift-off and drop into the ocean, using parachutes to slow them so they will not break up, but can be retrieved by ships and used again on another shuttle launch.

5. Orbital Maneuvering System (OMS)—These are two smaller rocket engines that "steer" the Orbiter into the right path for orbit. They were used to slow the Orbiter down or speed it up while it orbits the earth, as well as help it re-enter the atmosphere during landing.

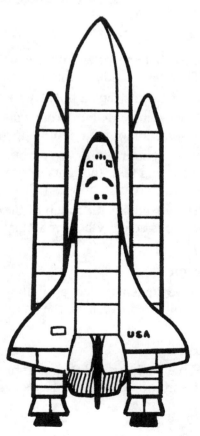

Toys in Space

Question

What is it like to be aboard the space shuttle?

Setting the Stage

- Take students to the playground, divide them into eight groups, and give each group a small ball to toss.
- After a few minutes, ask students to discuss what they think it would be like to play ball on the space shuttle.
- Explain to students one of the shuttle missions took a set of 12 toys into space to demonstrate how they would behave in the microgravity of space.
- Tell students that they will test some of these toys. Have them describe how they might behave if used aboard the space shuttle, and then have them view a video of astronauts demonstrating them in the mid-deck of the shuttle.

Materials Needed for Entire Group

- variety of toys (e.g., ball and jacks, flipping windup toy, gyroscope, magnetic marbles, paddleball, top, yo-yo, wheelo, etc.)
- paper for airplane (one per student)
- videotape of the 1985 STS - 51D mission of the shuttle showing Toys in Space (See Resources, page 88 for address of NASA.)
- data-capture sheet (page 49), one per student

Procedure

1. Distribute paper and have each student make an airplane according to his or her own design. Then have students line up across the back of the room, a few at a time, and fly their airplanes.
2. Let students repeat this, flying the planes backwards to see how they fly.
3. Divide students into groups and distribute data-capture sheets. Then have them write a description of what will happen to the paper plane in space.
4. Place the remaining toys around the classroom and have students rotate through these centers, recording their thoughts of how the toy would react in space on their data-capture sheets, before moving to another toy. (This may be done over several days.)
5. Show students the video of the mission that demonstrated the toys. Have the students record how the toys actually behaved in space on their data-capture sheets.

Extension

Have students select a toy they use or think of a game they play on Earth and describe how it would be different in the space shuttle.

Closure

Have students add their completed data-capture sheets to their space journals along with the description of the toy they selected for the extension activity.

48

Toys in Space *(cont.)*

You have been invited aboard the space shuttle to play with the toys shown below. Before the flight, you need to write how they behave on Earth and predict how they might behave when they are used in space. After your flight, you need to describe what you observed the toys do when being used on the shuttle.

TOY	OBSERVED ON EARTH	PREDICTION ON SHUTTLE	OBSERVED ON SHUTTLE
Ball and Jacks			
Gyroscope			
Paddleball			
Paper Plane			
Magnetic Marbles			
Top			
Slinky			
Wheelo			
Windup Toy			
Yo-yo			

 #639 Space—Intermediate

Classroom in Space

Question

What would it be like to have a classroom in space?

Setting the Stage
- Review with students the data-capture sheet from the activity How Much Do You Weigh? so they remember that the greater the mass, the greater the gravitational pull—e.g., Jupiter has the strongest gravity pull of the planets, Pluto the least.
- Explain to students everything has a gravitational pull, no matter how little the mass. When we move further away from the Earth, its pull becomes less. We would therefore float inside the space shuttle, but the shuttle does have a gravity pull. This is called microgravity. Something of a small mass, such as droplets of water, would be pulled to the walls of the shuttle, but people would float freely inside it. Remind students of the videos they saw.
- Tell students in this activity, they are going to imagine what it would be like to have a classroom in space.

Materials Needed for Each Individual
- colored markers or crayons
- ruler
- pencil
- compass
- pictures of astronauts floating in space shuttle
- data-capture sheet (page 51), one per student

Procedure
1. Distribute the data-capture sheet to each student.
2. Monitor students' progress as they work to offer assistance when needed.

Extensions
- Have students share their pictures with the rest of the class.
- Tell students to write a letter to someone on Earth describing what it is like to have a classroom in space.

Closure

Have students complete their data-capture sheets and add them to their space journals.

Classroom in Space *(cont.)*

Someday, children will live aboard space stations with their families. They will still need to learn. How do you think their school will be different from yours? Complete the information below, then make a drawing of your Classroom in Space.

List some ways a classroom of the future in space would be different from yours today:

1. _____ 4. _____
2. _____ 5. _____
3. _____ 6. _____

Tell what you could study in science in space better than you can on Earth:

1. _____ 4. _____
2. _____ 5. _____
3. _____ 6. _____

What type of physical education activities could you do in space that you cannot do on Earth?

1. _____ 4. _____
2. _____ 5. _____
3. _____ 6. _____

MY CLASSROOM IN SPACE

Just the Facts

There is a very good chance that when you are an adult, you or a friend will travel to the moon. This trip may be a permanent move to a moon base where people will live and work. There are some very important differences between Earth and the moon that must be considered before constructing a moon base. These were studied before NASA sent astronauts to the moon during the Apollo missions of 1969-1972, so that people could land on the moon, spend a few days, and return safely to Earth. These include:

- The moon has less mass than Earth, so everything would weigh 1/6 what it does on Earth. This means you can lift a lot more than you can on Earth and jump much higher, too.

- There is no atmosphere on the moon, so you must wear a pressurized suit that completely covers your body, even your hands, feet, and head. Buildings must be pressurized, like airplanes, to avoid the need for spacesuits all the time.

- A day at any location on the moon is about 15 days long, and there are about 15 days of night. The temperatures are extreme on the moon. It is 260^0 F (126^0 C) when the sun shines and -280^0 F (-137^0 C) when you step into a shadow or it is night. Living quarters must be insulated against these extremes of temperature, or you would freeze or roast.

- There is no atmosphere to scatter the sun's light, so the sky is totally black. Without atmosphere, sunlight would be super bright and you would get more harmful radiation from the sun than we do on Earth. This means special protection against the harmful rays from the sun is needed for eyes and body. Buildings could be constructed underground to help protect people from the temperature changes and sun's radiation.

- Since there is no air to carry sound, you would need to talk over a radio unless you are inside a building where there is air.

- The moon would be the perfect location for a telescope, since you never need to worry about clouds. When it is dark, you would have a much better view of the stars and planets than you would have from any observatory on Earth. You could also study the Earth from the moon. It would appear nearly four times as large as the moon appears to us. Earth would go through phases just like the moon does. Can you imagine what phase of Earth you would see when someone on Earth sees a full moon?

- Traveling over the surface of the moon would be difficult since there are so many large and small craters and boulders. Special "moon buggies" would be needed that could travel over this rough terrain. Gasoline engines will not work on the moon; they require air to make them run. The vehicles could use solar batteries when there is sunlight.

- There is no water on the moon, so it would need to be manufactured from moon rocks that contain hydrogen and oxygen.

- The moon is constantly being struck by a rain of meteors, most of which are very tiny. You would need protection from these as you moved around the moon or when outside buildings. The surface of the moon is covered with a fine dust that clings to clothes and equipment. This dust could cause problems if it gets into the moving parts of the equipment or into human lungs.

Phases of the Moon

Question

Why does the moon change its shape?

Setting the Stage

- Have students draw the various shapes they have seen the moon take. Let some of the students draw these examples on the board.
- Ask students to now draw what they think happens to change the shape of the moon.
- Tell students this lesson is designed to help them understand the cause of the phases of the moon.

Materials Needed for Each Group

- one set of Moon Phase Cutouts (page 54)
- clamp-on light fixture with 150 watt bulb
- 2" (5 cm) styrofoam ball glued to a stick for each student
- copy of The Phases of the Moon (page 55), one per student

Procedure

1. Divide students into eight groups and distribute the Moon Phase Cutouts (page 54).
2. Tell students to assemble the phases in a row in the order of their appearance during a complete cycle.
3. Have students hang the clamp-on light high at one end of the room, and then darken the room.
4. Have students leave their cutouts at their desks and assemble near the light.
5. Give each student a styrofoam ball on a stick and tell them it represents the moon.
6. Explain to students the ball is the moon, the light is the sun, and that their head is the Earth, with their city on the tip of their nose.
7. Turn out all the lights and have the students watch you as you demonstrate how to create the phases of the moon as follows, turning slowly counterclockwise:
   - New—holding the ball above your head and in front of your face, block out the light.
   - First Quarter—turn 90^0 from the first position, holding the ball at the same height.
   - Full—turn 180^0 from the sun, hold the ball above your head and in front of your face.
   - Last Quarter—turn 270^0 from the first position, holding the ball at the same height.
8. Have students follow your directions as they move, and pause at each phase to examine the shadow on the moon. Be sure they see that the shadow is on the left side of the first quarter and the right side of the last quarter.
9. Let students create the phases of the moon several times in the same sequence. Then, when you feel they are ready, call out a phase for them to show you.

Extension

Have students do the exercise "The Moon" from the Station-to-Station Activities section of this book (page 76).

Closure

In their space journals, have students make a set of moon phases showing the correct order from new moon to new moon.

Phases of the Moon *(cont.)*

Moon Phase Cutouts

The moon phases shown below are to be copied to make eight sets. You as the teacher should cut these out and number them as separate sets to avoid mixing them. You may wish to enclose each set in an envelope with its number on the outside. Divide students into eight groups and distribute a set of phases to each of them.

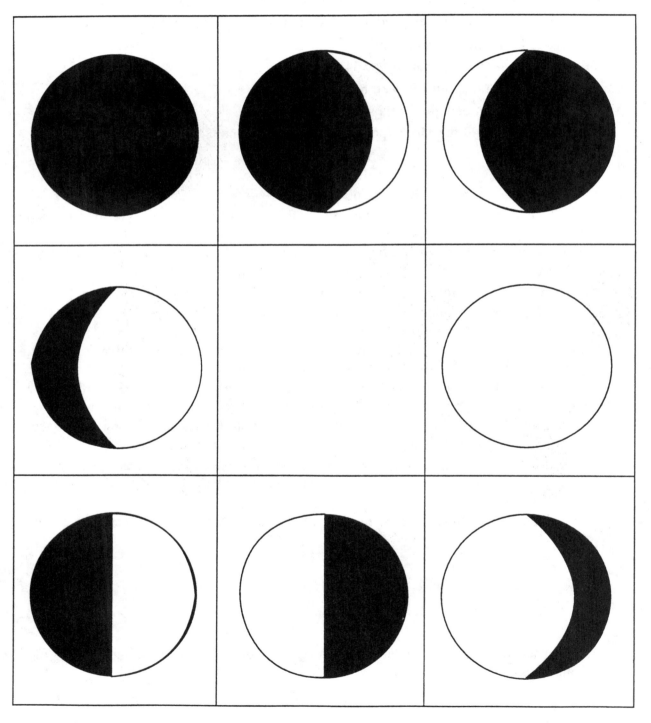

Phases of the Moon *(cont.)*

The Phases of the Moon

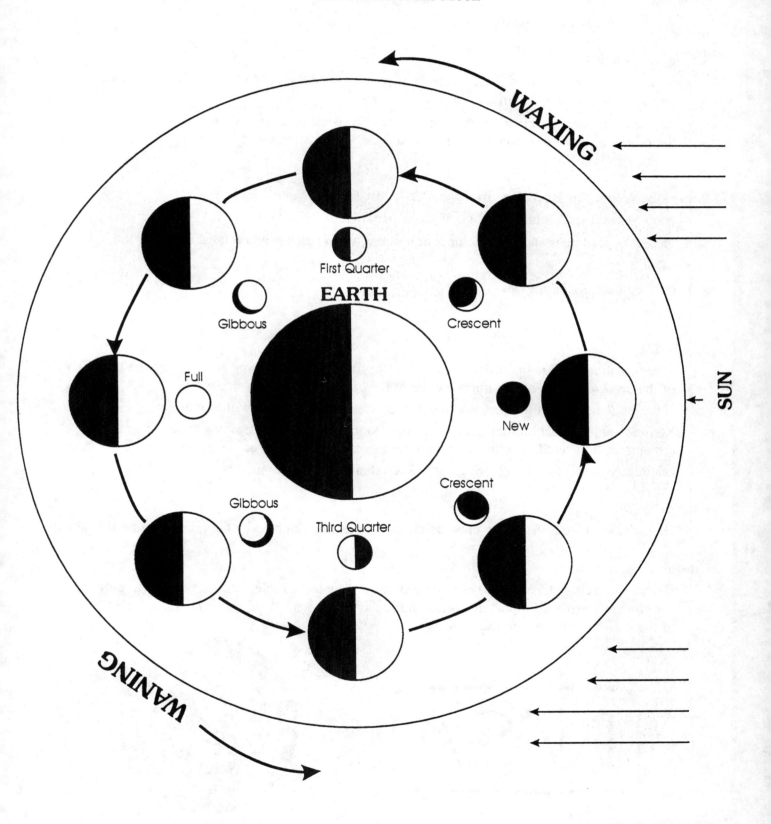

Creating a Crew Patch

Question

What should our crew patch look like?

Setting the Stage

- Show students pictures of some of the crew patches used during a variety of NASA missions, including the *Apollo*/Saturn missions to the moon.
- Explain to students each space mission crew has a specific patch designed for it. The names on the patch are those of the crew members, and the symbols represent something about the purpose of the mission.

Materials Needed for Each Group

- copy of crew patch outlines (page 57), one per student
- variety of resources showing pictures of space mission patches and related activities
- ruler
- colored markers or crayons
- compass

Procedure

1. Students should agree upon fictitious names for the four crew members and place the last names of the crew members on the outside edge of the crew patch.
2. Have students look at the pictures to get ideas of what their patch will look like.
3. Remind students that on their mission to the moon the crew will deploy a series of communication satellites in orbit around the moon and then land at the moon base.
4. Encourage students to be creative but to keep their pictures simple.

Extension

Have students wear their own crew patch, as well as that selected by the group, during the launch.

Closure

Before the crew patches have been colored, have a contest to select the crew patch to be worn by the crew and ground support members on the day of launch. Reproduce this for all the members of the crew to wear during the launch.

Creating a Crew Patch *(cont.)*

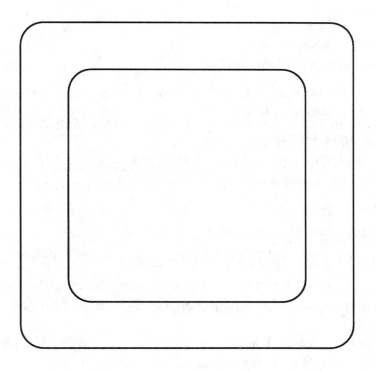

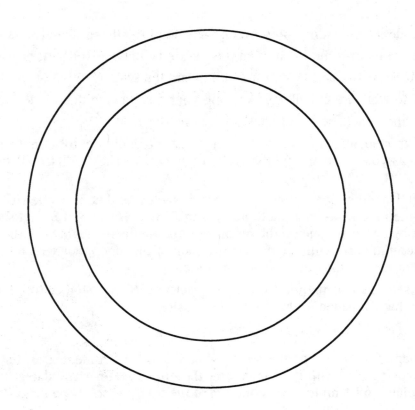

Finding a Landing Site

Question

Where are possible landing sites on the moon?

Setting the Stage

Tell students they will be plotting the landing sites of the six *Apollo* landings that took place between July, 1969, and December, 1972.

Materials Needed for Each Group

- copy of the Apollo Landing Sites map and data (page 59), one per student
- six self-adhesive dots (optional)

Materials Needed for Entire Class

- transparency of the Apollo Landing Sites (page 59)
- large map of the moon with coordinates shown (See Resources, pages 87-88.)

Procedure

1. Use the overhead transparency of Apollo Landing Sites (page 59) to explain the coordinate system to students.
2. Show students how to plot the landing site for *Apollo 11*, the first landing site on the moon.
3. Have students place a self-adhesive dot on this location or circle it in pencil.
4. Tell students to continue plotting the rest of the landing sites.

Extensions

- Explain to students all landing sites are on the side of the moon that always faces the earth.
- Demonstrate the moon's motion around the sun to the class as follows:
    - Tell students you are the moon and they are the Earth.
    - Begin to walk around, always keeping your face toward them.
    - Ask if they could see your back at anytime (no).
- Demonstrate to students what would happen if the moon did not turn on its axis at all by facing in one direction as you move around the group of students. They will see all sides of you in this case.
- Explain to students the moon turns on its axis in such way that only one side is visible from earth. The back of the moon was first photographed in 1959 by *Luna 3*, a Soviet satellite. Communications with anyone on the moon must be on line-of-sight with the Earth. It is not possible to communicate with anyone on the back of the moon, nor with a space vehicle when its orbit takes it around to the other side of the moon.
- Have students do the Curriculum Connections activity, Social Studies (page 70), which investigates what happened to the *Apollo 13* mission.

Closure

Put a large map of the moon on the bulletin board and have students transfer the data from their smaller maps using pins with flags that carry the *Apollo* number and date. Save this map to use with the simulated mission to the moon aboard the transporter. Then have students add their moon maps to their space journals.

Finding a Landing Site *(cont.)*

Apollo Landing Sites

Mark the location of each *Apollo* landing site, using the coordinates below.

MISSION	LATITUDE	LONGITUDE	AREA	DATE
Apollo 11	1° N	24° E	Sea of Tranquility	July, 1969
Apollo 12	3° S	23° W	Ocean of Storms	November, 1969
Apollo 14	4° S	18° W	Fra Mauro	January, 1971
Apollo 15	26° N	4° E	Hadley-Apennine	July, 1971
Apollo 16	9° S	16° E	Descartes	April, 1972
Apollo 17	20° N	30° E	Taulus-Littrow	December, 1972

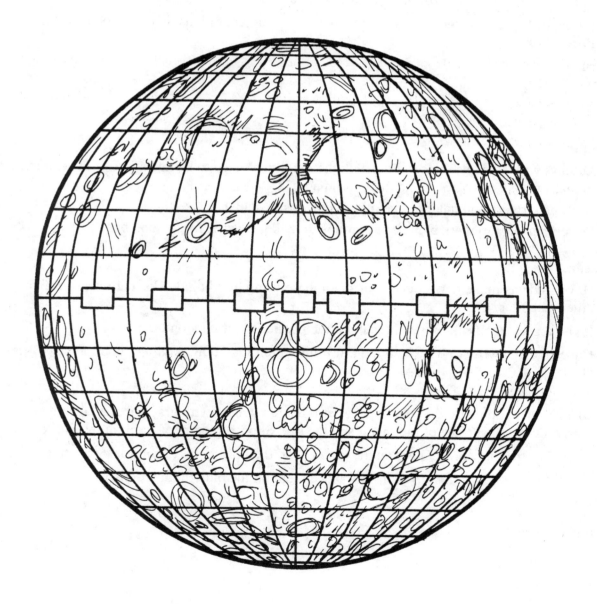

59

Sea of Tranquility—Moon Base

Question

> What would a moon base look like?

Setting the Stage

- Remind students of the time line they made in the activity The Great Space Race.
- Have students view a NASA videotape of one of the *Apollo 15, 16*, or *17* missions showing the *luna*r rover being used.
- Tell students they are going to design a moon base that will be in use by 2021.

Materials Needed for Each Individual

- videotape of *Apollo 15, 16*, or *17* missions (See Resources, pages 87-88.)
- reference books that show possible moon stations and conditions on the moon (See bibliography, pages 85-86.)
- ruler
- colored markers or crayons
- data-capture sheet (page 61)

Procedure

1. Discuss with students the conditions on the moon that need to be taken into consideration for humans to live there. (See Just the Facts, page 52.)
2. Distribute rulers and colored markers or crayons to students.
3. Permit students to work alone or in groups to make a design for a moon base.

Extensions

- Have students make a model of their moon base using building blocks, cartons, styrofoam, and other materials.
- Invite a guest to speak to the class about the possibility of a moon base.
- Have students write to NASA to request information regarding possible future moon bases.

Closure

- Display the moon base designs on a bulletin board covered with gray paper against black, representing the surface of the moon and the sky. Show a picture of Earth in the black sky.
- Have the students draw craters on the gray paper, then place the various designs on it.
- Have students design *luna*r rovers and place them on the bulletin board display.

Sea of Tranquility—Moon Base *(cont.)*

Read Just the Facts (page 52) and think about the type of moon base that should be built to safely house you and others who may be living on the moon someday. Decide where the living areas will be located, perhaps underground to give the most protection from the sun's radiation and extreme heat and cold. Select a particular area of the moon base from the list below and design it in detail:

- Living quarters for at least 50 people
- Recreation and entertainment
- School for adults and children
- Observatory and other science research labs
- Medical facilities
- Factory
- Stores
- Other of your choice

Draw your design of a moon base area. Give your drawing a title and describe it.

You Are Go for Launch!

Question

What is it like to launch into space?

Setting the Stage

- Display for students pictures of launches of various space missions.
- Ask students to imagine how it must feel to be an astronaut aboard these vehicles.
- Explain to students this lesson will lead them through a simulated launch of a space vehicle that is headed for the moon.

Materials Needed for Entire Class

- transparency of Mission Overview (page 64)
- copies of Moon Transport Mission Script for each participant in the simulation with their part highlighted (pages 65-68), one per student
- optional: copies of the script for the audience of students
- photographs of various manned space missions launchings (See Resources, pages 87-88.)
- slides showing the moon and Earth from space (See Resources, pages 87-88.)
- four sets of paper/cloth coveralls and gloves (See Resources, pages 87-88.)
- crew patches for each student (made in previous lesson)
- six rubber balloons filled with helium
- large box or garbage can capable of holding the balloons

Teacher Preparation

- Have students help decorate the four flight spacesuits with the crew patch and labels of the U.S. flag and emblem of NASA or another space agency they invent.
- Use large gloves, boots, and helmet fashioned from a suitable box for the astronaut who will deploy the satellite.
- Enlarge the two route maps and display them in front of the audience during the simulation.
- Divide your classroom into four areas as shown below:
    - Mission control—three students
    - Launch control—two students
    - Moon Transport—four students
    - Viewing—remainder of students

Procedure

1. Have the crew and control members take their places. Crew members should be in their flight spacesuits during launch and landing.
2. Provide students with background about the launch sequence, using a transparency of the Mission Overview (page 64).
3. Conduct the simulation by having crew and control members read their script while the navigator plots the path by moving a marker along the numbers on the map according to the script.

You Are Go for Launch! *(cont.)*

Extensions

- Have students produce a play using this script and adding slides of sights of Earth and moon that they would see on the way. (See Resources, pages 87-88.)

- Have students make paper instruments for the flight panel and paste these on large cardboard sheets to put in front of the commander and pilot.

Closure

Have a new set of students continue the simulation when transporter reaches moon.

You Are Go for Launch! *(cont.)*

MISSION OVERVIEW

- Space vehicle being launched: Transporter *Luna* carrying four crew members to the moon
- Launch site: Kennedy Space Center in Florida
- Date of Launch: July 20, 2021 (52 years after the first landing on the moon)
- Landing site: Sea of Tranquility Base on the moon
- Length of trip: five days
- Crew assignments during mission:
  - ✓ photograph Earth and moon from *Luna*
  - ✓ deploy series of satellites while in orbit around the moon

LAUNCH CODE

APU: **Auxiliary Power Unit** (power unit used before launch)
BFS: **Back-Up Flight System** (computer)
CSM: **Command Service Module** (where crew live during transport)
OPS: **Onboard Program System** (computer)
T: **Time** (T - [minus] before launch and T+ [plus] after launch)

MISSION COORDINATORS

LC: **Launch Control** (at Kennedy Space Center controls launch)
LLC: *Luna*r **Landing Control** (at Sea of Tranquility on moon, controls lunar landing)
MC: **Mission Control** (at Houston Space Center, controls mission after launch)
PAO: **Public Affairs Officer** (announces events of mission to the public)
NAV: **Navigator** (shows progress of flight during the mission)

CREW MEMBERS

Commander: Chief pilot in charge of entire flight
Pilot: Second in command of flight
MS: Mission Specialist (in charge of payload deployment during mission)
PS: Payload Specialist (helps with inflight mission assignments)

You Are Go for Launch! *(cont.)*

Moon Transport Mission Script

PAO:	It is now T minus 1 hour, 30 minutes, beginning the final countdown for the launch of the space transport *Luna*.
LC:	*Luna*, this is Launch Control radio check.
Commander:	Launch Control, this is *Luna*. We read you loud and clear.
MC:	*Luna*, this is Mission Control radio check.
Commander:	Mission Control, we read you loud and clear.
LC:	*Luna*, ready for abort advisory check.
Pilot:	Roger. Abort advisory check is satisfactory.
LC:	*Luna*, this is Launch Control. Side hatch is secure.
Commander:	We copy, Launch Control.
MS:	Launch Control, cabin pressure is fine.
LC:	Roger. We copy.
PS:	Boiler control switch on. Nitrogen supply switch on.
LC:	Roger. We copy.
Pilot:	OMS pressure is on.
MS:	Launch Control, this is *Luna*. Cabin vent check complete.
LC:	Roger, *Luna*.
PAO:	The count is at T minus 22 minutes, 16 seconds and holding. This is a planned hold built into the countdown to allow all sequences to be completed before proceeding. The navigator will show us the location of the transporter *Luna* on the map. After the launch, the navigator will continue to move the marker to show where *Luna* is in space, until it lands on the moon.
NAV #1:	(Place pin on *Luna*r Transporter map on #1 position to show location of *Luna*)
Commander:	Control, *Luna*'s flight plan is loaded into the computer.
LC:	Resume countdown.
Commander:	Control, this is *Luna*, OPS-1 loaded into BFS
LC:	Roger. We copy.
PAO:	T minus 12 minutes and 29 seconds and counting.
LC:	This is Control, *Luna*, conducting the abort check.
Pilot:	Roger. Looks good from here.
PAO:	It is T minus 9 minutes and holding. At this point, there is a scheduled one-minute hold to allow one last chance to catch up before the final part of the countdown begins.
LC:	It is a go for Launch. Resume countdown.
Commander:	Control, we have activated event time.
LC:	Roger. Crew access arm is being retracted. Time to initiate APU prestart procedure, *Luna*.
Commander:	Roger, control. Prestart complete, APUs powered up.
LC:	Roger.
Pilot:	APUs look good.
LC:	This is Control. You are on internal power.
Commander:	Crew, you are go to put your visors down.
Pilot:	**<u>Launch Control, we have a problem here. The pressure gauge shows a drop in cabin pressure.</u>**
LC:	Please repeat your message.

65

You Are Go for Launch! *(cont.)*

Moon Transport Mission Script *(cont.)*

Pilot:	<u>**We have a problem here. The cabin pressure has dropped.**</u>
PAO:	There is a drop in the cabin pressure of the transport. This sometimes happens when the crew members put their visors down and begin to breathe pure oxygen. The countdown will be held until the problem is checked out.
Pilot:	Control, this is *Luna*. Happy to report the cabin pressure is OK!
LC:	*Luna*, we copy you. The countdown will be resumed.
Commander:	Roger, Control.
LC:	*Luna*, this is Control. Hydraulic check complete.
Pilot:	Roger.
LC:	*Luna*, this is Control. Main engines gimbal complete.
Pilot:	Roger. We copy.
LC:	*Luna*, this is Control. Oxygen-two vents closed and looking good.
Pilot:	Roger.
PAO:	We are at T minus 2 minutes, 10 seconds and counting. The moon at this precise second is 218,986 mi (350,378 km) away.
LC:	<u>**You are GO FOR LAUNCH.**</u>
Commander:	<u>**Roger. Understand we are GO FOR LAUNCH.**</u> We are looking forward to a great flight.
LC:	*Luna*, this is Control. APU start is go. Onboard computer switched on.
Commander:	Roger.
LC:	Beginning the count at 10 seconds, 9, 8, 7, 6, 5, 4, 3, 2...1...zero. **LIFTOFF!**

NAV #2

PAO:	<u>**We have liftoff of the space transport *Luna*. GO, baby, go!**</u> Great storms of burning fuel, orange, and red in the gray-black smoke are billowing out of the rocket. There are 50,000 gal (200,000 L) of water a minute being sprayed on the launch site to keep it from burning up.
LC:	All engines are looking good. Instituting maneuver for orbit angle. Orbit maneuver completed *Luna*, you look *good*.

NAV #3

Commander:	Control, this is *Luna*. Beginning roll program.
PAO:	Onboard guidance systems are now tipping the transport slightly to fly southeast over the Atlantic. We now transfer to Houston for Mission Control to take over the mission.
MC:	Roger. We are at 1 minute and 11 seconds into the flight.
Commander:	Control, this is *Luna*. Roll completed and pitch is programmed.
MC:	Roger. We copy. Thrust is go, all engines.
Commander:	Roger. Full thrust all engines. First stage is now falling away. Second stage firing.

You Are Go for Launch! *(cont.)*

Moon Transport Mission Script *(cont.)*

NAV #4

Commander:	Mission Control, **we are in orbit!**
MC:	Roger. We copy. It is T +12 minutes; orbit has been achieved. Throttle back and release second stage.
Pilot:	Mission Control, this is *Luna*. We have throttled back. Second stage is away. Orbit speed is 17,500 mph (28,000 kmph).
MC:	Roger. We copy that.

NAV #5

PAO:	The transporter will be parked in an orbit 120 miles (192 km) above Earth until it is time to fire the third stage rocket to send it toward the moon.
MC:	This is Mission Control. *Luna*, check systems in CSM and third stage rocket.
Commander:	Roger. CSM systems and rocket check OK.
MC:	This is Mission Control, third stage rocket ignition at 5...4...3...2...1...**Fire!**
Pilot:	Ignition is successful. WOW! **What a kick!**

NAV #6

Commander:	Our speed is now 24,400 mph (39,040 kmph)! We are leaving Earth's orbit and heading toward the moon.
Pilot:	Third stage away. We will float toward the moon now.
MC:	Roger. Good luck on your 225,000 mi (360,000 km) journey.

NAV #7

- - - - - - - - -PAUSE - - - - - - - -

PAO:	It is two days after the launch, and the transporter is being slowed by the pull of Earth's gravity.
Commander:	Mission Control, this is *Luna*. Our speed is now 2,300 mph (3,680 kmph).
MC:	Roger. You will soon be picked up by the moon's gravity.

- - - - - - - - -PAUSE- - - - - - - -

PAO:	Three days have passed since the launch at Kennedy Space Center.
Pilot:	Control, we are feeling the pull of the moon, and it is increasing our speed.

NAV #8

MC:	Prepare to fire service module engines as you come around the moon.
PAO:	This burn will take place on the back side of the moon and since no communication can pass through the moon to Earth, the commander will control the countdown. Only after the transporter has come from behind the moon will we know if the engines fired successfully.

NAV #9

Pilot:	Engines fired on time, and we are in orbit around the moon!
PAO:	At this time, the payload specialist assists the mission specialist into the spacesuit to leave the transport and deploy a series of satellites that will orbit the moon to make it possible to communicate with all areas of the moon.

You Are Go for Launch! *(cont.)*

Moon Transport Mission Script *(cont.)*

NAV #10

The mission specialist moves through the airlock and steps out into the emptiness of space. Only a thin line is needed to keep the astronaut from floating away from the spacecraft.

PS: How are you doing out there?

MS: I feel great! **The view is magnificent**. The Earth looks like a small blue marble from here. The moon is enormous.

NAV #11: **Oh, look at that! I can see the moon base below me!**

PS: You're right. That is a spectacular view! Prepare to deploy satellites. Do not lose them. Remember, they cost millions of dollars!

MS: Don't worry. I wouldn't lose any.

NAV #12: Deploying satellites now.

PS: Satellites look good from here. Data readings are good. You can float around out there and enjoy the scenery for a while. Do not forget to keep your line hooked to the transporter. I'll let you know when to reel the satellite back.

Pilot: Looks like he is really enjoying himself out there.

NAV #13: Do not float away too far. It's a long way home from here.

- - - - PAUSE - - - - - - - -

PS: Time to come back inside and prepare for lunar landing.

NAV #14

PAO: The crew of *Luna* has been in orbit for one day around the moon and is now preparing to land at the Sea of Tranquility Moon Base.

Commander: All crew members return to your seats and prepare for retrorocket burn.

NAV #15: *Luna*r Landing Control, this is *Luna*. Retrorocket burn complete.

LLC: Roger. We copy. We'll be glad to have you join us at the base. Call out your altitude as you near landing.

Pilot: We are at 500 feet, 400...300...200...100.

NAV #16

Commander: Landing gear down and locked.
Pilot: **Contact. *Luna* has landed!**
LLC: **Welcome to the Sea of Tranquility Moon Base.**

NAV #17

PAO: The transporter *Luna* has made a successful landing on the moon. The crew members will now transfer to the base and begin their work on the moon.

Language Arts

Communication skills will be needed to convey information between space travelers and Earth in the future, just as early explorers had to be able to describe their journeys. Students can develop a variety of ways to communicate via letters, drawings, and code. These messages may be directed at Earth or for intelligent life in other planetary systems.

Science Concept: A variety of techniques will be needed to communicate with Earth and intelligent life in other planetary systems in the future.

Letters From a Lunar Base

- Have students write a letter to someone on Earth describing their adventures as members of a science team working at Tranquility Base on the moon in the year 2021. Have them gather information about future lunar bases that can be used in their letters.
- Have students write to NASA to request material that describes the *Apollo* landings.
- Have students include drawings of their spacecraft, the lunar base, and views of Earth.
- Tell students to describe how it feels to walk about on the moon.

Letters to Another Planet

- Have students design a message that would communicate information about our planetary system and Earth to intelligent life on a planet that is not in our solar system.
- Explain to them they may wish to use pictures or diagrams that could be interpreted easily by someone who does not know about our solar system and cannot read any of our languages.

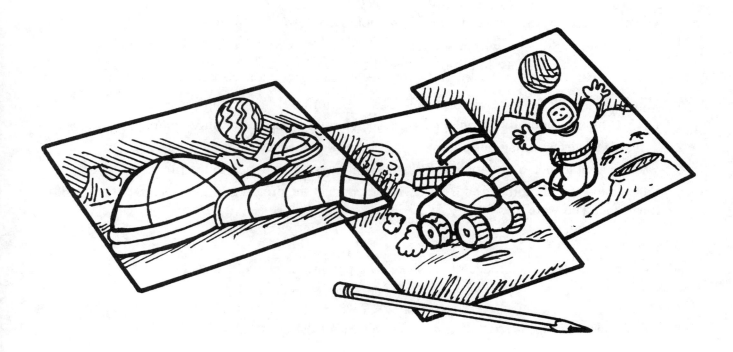

Social Studies

Houston! We've Had a Problem Here!

Science Concept: Problem-solving skills are needed when traveling in space.

The *Apollo 13* mission to the moon nearly ended in tragedy. Two days after launch, and 200,000 miles (320,000 km) from Earth, there was an explosion of a liquid oxygen tank in the service module, destroying the fuel cells that supplied power to the spacecraft and cutting off the oxygen supply. This is an exciting adventure for students to investigate. It shows the need for problem-solving skills and courage when traveling in space.

Question

What happened to the *Apollo 13* mission to the moon?

Setting the Stage

- Show students the large moon map used to plot the landing sites of the *Apollo* missions on the moon.

- Ask students how many landings were made (six).

- Tell students there were supposed to be seven, but the *Apollo 13* mission never landed.

- Explain to students they are going to collect all the information they can find about this mission and write a newspaper article that describes it.

Materials Needed for Each Group

- resource books and periodicals that tell about the *Apollo 13* mission. Two examples follow:
  - ✓ Kerrod, Robin. *The Illustrated History of NASA*. Gallery Books, 1988.
  - ✓ *Life in Space*, Time-Life Books, Inc., 1983.
- videotape from NASA about *Apollo 13* mission (See Resources, pages 87-88.)

Note to the teacher: Students will investigate the details of this near-tragic mission and write a script for a television news broadcast to present to the class.

Procedure

1. Divide students into groups and let them research information regarding *Apollo 13*.
2. Tell students to prepare a script for a television news broadcast about this mission.
3. Encourage students to find pictures or make drawings that will add to their report.
4. Suggest to students some groups may wish to conduct the program as an interview of some of the astronauts who were involved.

Extension

Videotape some of the broadcasts to share with parents or other classrooms.

Closure

Have student groups present their news broadcast for the class.

Physical Education

Let students experience how difficult it is to launch and land a vehicle on the moon by experiencing a simulation of this task.

Science Concept: The moon travels around the Earth approximately every 28 days. The Earth spins on its axis once every 24 hours and travels around the sun in 365 1/4 days.

Note to the teacher:

The teacher will need to sketch two concentric circles on the playground. One circle should be a diameter of 3' (1 m) inside a circle 10' (3 m) in diameter.

This lesson can also be conducted on a simple children's merry-go-round often found at a neighborhood park.

- Have your class assemble around the large circle, leaving about 5' (1.5 m) of space between them and the edge of the circle.

- Select two students, one to represent the Earth and the other the moon.

- Have *Earth* stand on the edge of the inside circle and *Moon* on the outside circle.

- They should toss a tennis ball back and forth to practice catching it while standing still.

- Once students become adept at catching the ball, have *Earth* begin to move around its circle in a counterclockwise direction, continuing to toss and catch the ball.

- Now, simulate the launch and landing of a lunar vehicle by having *Moon* walk slowly around the larger circle, in the same direction as *Earth*. Continue tossing the *Lunar Transporter* between *Earth* and *Moon*.

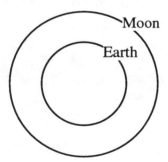

- This simulates a real life dilemma of launching a space vehicle from the moving Earth and landing it on the moon, which is moving around the Earth during the three days required to make the trip.

Math

How High Is the Sun?

Science Concept:

In the northern hemisphere, the sun is highest in the sky on the first day of summer (June 21) and lowest in the sky on the first day of winter (December 21).

Measurements can be made with the shadow stick used in the lesson "Our Star, the Sun" to determine how high the sun is above the horizon. By measuring and recording this once a month at noon (using daylight standard time), students will realize that the sun's position changes throughout the year. The measurement should be done as close to the 21st of each month as possible to coincide with the first days of summer and winter. Two or three days before or after the 21st will still provide adequate data.

Setting the Stage
- Conduct the lesson: "Our Star, the Sun."
- Familiarize students with protractors so they can measure angles.

Materials Needed for Each Group
- protractors (These may be copied on overhead transparencies to make sturdy and inexpensive copies for each student to use. Cut off the ruler portion of the protractor before copying it to make measuring angles more accurate.)
- shadow stick
- length of string that can reach from the tip of the shadow to the top of the stick
- data-capture sheet (page 73), one per student

Procedure
1. Have students become familiar with learning how to measure angles.
2. Divide students into eight groups and demonstrate where to place the string and protractor to measure the sun's angular height above the horizon:

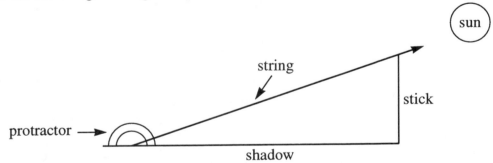

3. Distribute and have students complete a data-capture sheet.
4. Have students collect data over an eight- or ten-month period.

Closure

Have students place their completed data-capture sheets in their space journals.

Math *(cont.)*

Make your measurements as close to the 21st of each month as possible. You should also measure the angle as close to noon as you can. Remember, if you are on daylight savings time (April–October), you will need to subtract an hour to determine when noon occurs.

DATE	TIME	ANGLE OF SUN ABOVE HORIZON
_____	_____	_____ °
_____	_____	_____ °
_____	_____	_____ °
_____	_____	_____ °
_____	_____	_____ °
_____	_____	_____ °
_____	_____	_____ °
_____	_____	_____ °
_____	_____	_____ °

Use the data you have collected to make a graph showing the changing position of the sun at noon through the months you recorded. An example of what this graph might look like is shown below:

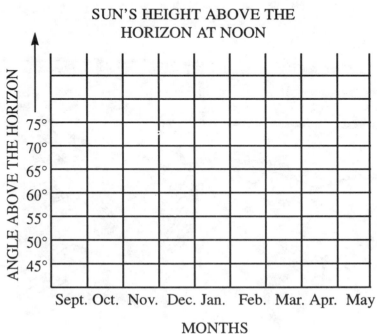

Look at your graph and write a description of what it shows you about the sun's location in the sky through these months. Find the hours of daylight for each of these dates in an almanac.

Art

Space Transportation Systems

Students enjoy designing space vehicles. This lesson incorporates their artistic talents as well as investigative skills to research the possibilities of space travel.

Science Concept: Space travel will become more common in the near future.

- Divide your class into groups and have them design space vehicles to be used for trips between Earth and the moon or from the moon to Mars. Have them research the variety of space vehicles that have already been developed and tested, as well as those being designed for future space travel. Then have them investigate the *Viking* missions that landed on Mars and the *Apollo* missions that went to the moon to gather information for the requirements for these transportation systems, including the following:

  ✓ Length of the trip
  ✓ Distances to be traveled
  ✓ Number of passengers
  ✓ Launch and landing requirements

- Have students draw their vehicles from different views (above, side, and in front).

- Tell students to show an interior view as well, showing areas for passengers and crew.

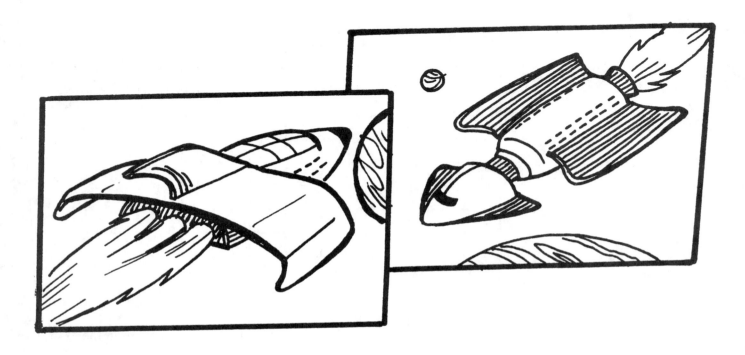

74

Final Assessment

To the Student: You will need to refer to the Space Exploration Time Line (pages 89-96) and Scale Model of the Planets (page 17), as well as your space journal to complete this assessment.

Name: _____ _____ Date: _____

Our Solar System

Look at the "Scale Model of the Planets" (pages 17-19) and list them in order of size beginning with the largest:

1. _____   4. _____   7. _____

2. _____   5. _____   8. _____

3. _____   6. _____   9. _____

Choose any two planets except Earth and describe them below:

Planet #1: _____   Planet #2: _____

My weight
on planet #1: _____

My weight
on planet #2: _____

Its diameter: _____

Its diameter: _____

It is the _____th planet from the sun.

It is the _____th planet from the sun.

It is _____ AU from the sun.

It is _____ AU from the sun.

On the back of this page, write a newspaper article describing one of the planets above.

History of Space Exploration

Look at the Space Exploration Time Line and tell what the three peak years of space activity were:

1. _____   2. _____   3. _____

Draw a picture of your favorite space event below, and then describe it:

_____

_____

Final Assessment *(cont.)*

Space Shuttle

Draw a picture of yourself aboard the space shuttle. Tell what you are doing in the picture.

_____

_____

The Moon

Look at the moon phases below and place a number below them to put them in the correct order:

1   #_____   #_____   #_____

Draw a picture of yourself walking on the moon, and then tell how it is different from walking on Earth.

Science Safety

Discuss the necessity for science safety rules. Reinforce the rules on this page or adapt them to meet the needs of your classroom. You may wish to reproduce the rules for each student or post them in the classroom.

1. Begin science activities only after all directions have been given.

2. Never put anything in your mouth unless it is required by the science experience.

3. Always wear safety goggles when participating in any lab experience.

4. Dispose of waste and recyclables in proper containers.

5. Follow classroom rules of behavior while participating In science experiences.

6. Review your basic class safety rules every time you conduct a science experience.

You can still have fun and be safe at the same time!

Space Journal

Space Journals are an effective way to integrate science and language arts. Students are to record their observations, thoughts, and questions about past science experiences in a journal to be kept in the science area. The observations may be recorded in sentences or sketches which keep track of changes both in the science item or in the thoughts and discussions of the students.

Space Journal entries can be completed as a team effort or an individual activity. Be sure to model the making and recording of observations several times when introducing the journals to the science area.

Use the student recordings in the Space Journals as a focus for class science discussions. You should lead these discussions and guide students with probing questions, but it is usually not necessary for you to give any explanation. Students come to accurate conclusions as a result of classmates' comments and your questioning. Space Journals can also become part of the students' portfolios and overall assessment program. Journals are valuable assessment tools for parent and student conferences as well.

How To Make a Space Journal

1. Cut two pieces of 8.5 " x 11" (22 cm x 28 cm) construction paper to create a cover. Reproduce page 79 and glue it to the front cover of the journal. Allow students to draw space pictures in the box on the cover.
2. Insert several Space Journal pages. (See page 80.)
3. Staple together and cover stapled edge with book tape.

My
Space
Journal

Name _____

Space Journal

Illustration

This is what happened: _____

_____

_____

_____

_____

This is what I learned: _____

_____

_____

_____

_____

Space Observation Area

In addition to station-to-station activities, students should be given other opportunities for real-life science experiences. For example, models of rockets and the solar system can provide a vehicle for discovery learning if students are given enough time and space to observe them.

Set up a space observation area in your classroom. As children visit this area during open work time, expect to hear stimulating conversations and questions among them. Encourage curiosity but respect their independence!

Books with facts pertinent to the subject, item, or process being observed should be provided for students who are ready to research more sophisticated information.

Sometimes it is very stimulating to set up a science experiment or add something interesting to the Space Observation Area without a comment from you at all! If the experiment or materials in the observation area should not be disturbed, reinforce with students the need to observe without touching or picking up.

Super Space Scientist Award

This is to certify that

_____

Name

made a science discovery.

Congratulations!

_____

Teacher

_____

Date

SUPER SPACE SCIENTIST

82

Glossary

Astronomy—the study of everything in space beyond Earth, from our moon to the most distant stars and galaxies in the Universe.
Astronaut—a person who travels in space (American).
Atmosphere—the blanket of gases (air) around a planet or moon.
AU—astronomical unit, which is equal to the average distance between the Earth and the sun—93,000,000 mi (1,490,000,000 km).

Circumference—the distance around a circle or a sphere.
Cosmonaut—a person (Russian) who travels in space.
Conclusion—the outcome of an investigation.
Control—a standard measure of comparison in an experiment. The control always stays constant.

Diameter—the distance through the middle and from one side to the other of a circle or sphere.

Escape Velocity—the speed necessary to break away from a celestial body. For Earth this is about 25,000 mph (40,000 kmph).
EVA—extra-vehicular activity (EVA) is when astronauts work outside a spacecraft.
EVMU—extra vehicular mobility unit (space unit).
Experiment—a means of proving or disproving an hypothesis.

Gravity—the pull on all bodies towards the Earth's center.

Hypothesis (hi-POTH-e-sis)—an educated guess to a question you are trying to answer.

Investigation—an observation of something followed by a systematic inquiry in order to explain what was originally observed.

Mass—the total amount of material in any item.
Meteor—particles of material drifting through the solar system, often left over from a comet.

Glossary *(cont.)*

NASA—National Aeronautics and Space Administration.
Neil Armstrong—first man to set foot on the moon (July 20, 1969).
Newton's First Law of Motion—a body at rest will remain at rest, and a body in motion will remain in motion at a constant velocity unless acted upon by an unbalanced force.
Newton's Second Law of Motion—force equals mass times acceleration.
Newton's Third Law of Motion—for every action there is an opposite and equal reaction.

Observation—careful notice or examination of something.
Orbit—a curved path of one object around another, such as a planet around the sun or a spacecraft around Earth.

Planet—A heavenly body that orbits a star, such as the nine planets which orbit the sun. These are visible due to reflected light from the star.
Procedure—the series of steps carried out when doing an experiment.

Question—a formal way of inquiring about a particular topic.

Radius—The distance from the outside of a circle or sphere to its center, equal to one half the diameter.
Results—the data collected after performing an experiment.

Satellite—A natural or artificial body that orbits around a planet, such as moons or scientific spacecraft like *Voyager*.
Scientific Method—a systematic process of proving or disproving a given question, following an observation. Observation, question, hypothesis, procedure, results, conclusion, and future investigations.
Science-Process Skills—the skills necessary to have in order to be able to think critically. Process skills include: observing, communicating, comparing, ordering, categorizing, relating, inferring, and applying.
Solar System—our star system, which consists of nine planets, all orbiting the sun.
Spacecraft—a special vehicle designed to travel into space.
Star—a sphere of hot gases that gives off light. Some are smaller than the Earth, some larger than the orbit of Mars.
S T S—Space Transport System (STS) is another name for the space shuttle.
Sun—a star that is average in size and temperature compared to all other stars. All nine planets orbit around it and receive its light and heat in varying amounts, depending upon their distance from the sun.

Variable—the changing factor of an experiment.

Weight—the amount of heaviness or mass. Weight is dependent upon the amount of gravitational pull, but mass is not.

Bibliography

Abernathy, Susan. *Space Machines.* Western Pub., 1991.

Adams, Peter. *Moon, Mars, and Meteorites.* Cambridge University Press, 1984.

Asimov, Isaac. *Space Garbage.* Dell, 1991.

Baird, Anne. *Space Camp: The Great Adventures for NASA Hopefuls.* Morrow Bks, 1992.

Becklake, Sue. *Space, Stars, Planets & Spacecraft.* Dorling Kindersley, 1991.

Cole, Joanna. *The Magic School Bus Lost in the Solar System.* Scholastic Books, 1990.

Collins, Michael. *Liftoff; The Story of America's Adventure in Space.* NASA/Grove Press, 1988.

Donnelly, Judy. *Space Junk: Pollution Beyond the Earth.* Morrow Jr. Bks., 1990.

Fraier, Kendrick. *Solar System.* Time-Life Books, Inc., 1985.

Gallant, Roy. *Our Universe.* National Geographic Picture Atlas, 1986.

Gamiello, Elvira. *Space Age Mazes.* Kidsbks, 1989.

Joels, Kerry and others. *The Space Shuttle Operators Manual.* Ballantine Books, 1982.

Joels, Kerry. *The Mars One Crew Manual.* Ballantine Books, 1985.

Jones, Brian. *Space Exploration.* Gareth Stevens Inc., 1989.

Kerrod, Robin. *The Illustrated History of NASA.* Gallery Books, 1988.

Kerrod, Robin. *Living in Space.* Crescent Books, 1986.

Kerrod, Robin. *Spacecraft.* Random Bks Yng Readers, 1989.

Life in Space. Time-Life Books, Inc., 1983.

Lampton, Christopher. *Space Sciences.* Watts, 1983.

McCarter, James. *Space Shuttle Disaster.* Watts, 1988.

Packard, Edward. *Space Fortress.* Bantam, 1991.

Ride, Sally and others. *To Space and Back.* Shepard Books, 1986.

Sabin, Louis. *Space Exploration & Travel.* Troll Assocs., 1985.

Terman, Douglas. *Space & Beyond.* Bantam, 1987.

Vbrova, Zuza. *Space & Astronomy.* Watts, 1989.

Wroble, Lisa. *Space Science.* Capstone Press.

Zim, Herbert & Baker, Robert. *Stars.* Golden Press, 1985.

Bibliography *(cont.)*

Spanish Titles

Biesty, S. *Del interior de las cosas (Incredible Cross-Sections).* Santillana Pub. Co., 1993.

McDermott, G. *Flecha al sol (Arrow to the Sun).* Viking Press, 1974.

Tan, A. *La dama de la luna (Moon Lady).* Lectorum, 1992.

Technology

Broderbund. *Discover* and *Where In Space Is Carmen San Diego?* Available from Broderbund, (415)382-4530. software

D.C. Heath. *Traveling Through the Solar System.* Available from William K. Bradford Pub. Co., (800)421-2009. software

Deltron, Inc. *Bradford Sky Travel.* Available from William K. Bradford Pub. Co., (800)421-2009. software

Focus Media. *Planetarium on Computer: The Solar System.* Available from CDL Software Shop, (800)637-0047. software

January Productions. *Exploring Our Solar System.* Available from CDL Software Shop, (800)637-0047. software

MECC. *Rocket Factory.* Available from CDL Software Shop, (800)637-0047. software

National Geographic Society. *STV: Solar System.* Available from Sunburst, (800)321-7511. videodisc

Sliwa. *History of Space Flight.* Available from CDL Software Shop, (800)637-0047. software

Southwest EdPsych Services. *The Moon and Its Phases.* Available from CDL Software Shop, (800)637-0047. software

WDCN. *Journey into Space and Space Camp.* Available from AIT, (800)457-4509. video

Resources

Challenges for Space Explorers, a collection of activities for grades 4-12 focusing on living and working in space. Includes background information and reproducible pages. For a free copy, send your request on school letterhead to: Education Service Center, MRC 305, National Air and Space Museum, Washington, DC 20560.

Volcanoes on Mars, a slide set of geologic features, including images from the Viking missions. Available for purchase from: *Lunar* and Planetary Institute, 3303 NASA Road 1, Houston, TX 77058-4399. Request a list of other materials that are available.

Real Stuff, a 58-minute video, 1987. From the PBS series FRONTLINE, this program looks at the dangers of space flight and interviews shuttle astronauts. Available from: PBS VIDEO, 1320 Braddock Place, Alexandria, VA 22314-1698.

Skylab, Our First Space Station, NASA SP 400, 1977. Available from: NASA Headquarters, Washington, DC 20546.

Moon Kit, 1988, slides developed by the Astronomical Society of the Pacific. Available from: National Science Teachers Association, 1742 Connecticut Ave., NW, Washington, DC 20009. You may also request a free catalog of other materials that are available for purchase.

The Eagle Has Landed: The Flight of Apollo 11. Video (28 minutes), 1969. Available from NASA CORE, Lorain County Joint Vocational School, 15181 Route 58 South, Oberlin, OH 44014. (Request a list of other NASA videos that are available.)

Lunar Phenomena, slides on important aspects of the moon. Available from: MMI Corporation, 2950 Wyman Parkway, P.O. Box 19907, Baltimore, MD 21211.

Spacelink. NASA's Spacelink is an on-line information system for educators. Teachers can download many space-related lessons from Spacelink. Computer access number: (205) 895-0028. Modem settings: 8 data bits, no parity, 1 stop bit.

Video tapes and slides of space exploration by satellite and manned space flight. Contact Finley Holiday Films, P.O. Box 619, Whittier, CA 90608 to request list of materials and order form.

The Universe in the Classroom is a newsletter printed free for teachers. Contact: Teachers Newsletter Department, Astronomical Society of the Pacific (ASP), 390 Ashton Ave., San Francisco, CA 94112. You may also purchase a map of Mars from ASP. Request a catalog of astronomical and space slides, videos, and other materials.

Sky Calendar is a monthly calendar with daily illustrations of astronomical events. Annual subscription from: Abrams Planetarium, Michigan State University, East Lansing, MI 48824.

The Earth*'s Moon* relief map of the moon with coordinates and crater names, 42" x 28" (105 cm x 70 cm). Order #02276, National Geographic Society, PO Box 96094, Washington, DC 20077-9191.

Solar System Mobile with photographs from space of the sun and planets (except Pluto) may be purchased in science stores and museum shops or from Delta Education, Inc., PO Box 950, Hudson, NH, 03051-9924. (800)442-5444.

Model rocket engines and kits may be ordered from Estes Industries/Hi-Flier, 1295 H Street, Penrose, CO 81240.

Resources *(cont.)*

NASA Teacher Resource Centers

NASA Teacher Resource Centers (NTRC) are located across the nation. Teachers can preview or copy NASA prints, videos, and computer educational materials in almost every subject area at the centers. Request a list of materials and information available to teachers from the NASA TRC nearest you or from NASA CORE, Lorain County Joint Vocational School, 15181 Route 58 South, Oberlin, OH 44074.

NASA Teacher Resource Center
Mail Stop TO-25
NASA Ames Research Center
Moffett Field, CA 94035
Phone: (415) 604-3574

NASA Teacher Resource Center
Mail Code 130.3
NASA Goddard Space Flight Center
Greenbelt, MD 20771
Phone: (301) 286-8570

NASA Teacher Resource Center
Mail Code AP-4
NASA Johnson Space Center
Houston, TX 77058
Phone: (713) 483-8696

NASA Teacher Resource Center
Mail Code ERL
NASA Kennedy Space Center
Kennedy Space Center, FL 32899
Phone: (407) 867-4090

NASA Teacher Resource Center
Mail Stop 146
NASA Langley Research Center
Hampton, VA 23681-0001
Phone: (804) 864-3293

NASA Teacher Resource Center
Mail Stop 8-1
NASA Lewis Research Center
21000 Brookpark Road
Cleveland, OH 44135
Phone: (216) 433-2017

NASA Teacher Resource Center
Alabama Space and Rocket Center
Huntsville, AL 35807
Phone: (205) 544-5812

NASA Teacher Resource Center
Building 1200
NASA John C. Stennis Space Center
Stennis Space Center, MS 39529
Phone: (601) 688-3338

NASA Teacher Resource Center
JPL Educational Outreach
Mail Stop CS-530
Jet Propulsion Laboratory
4800 Oak Grove Drive
Pasadena, CA 91109
Phone: (818) 354-6916

NASA Dryden Flight Research Facility
Public Affairs Office (Trl. 42)
NASA Teacher Resource Center
Edwards, CA 93523
Phone: (805) 258-3456

Wallops Flight Facility
Education Complex - Visitor Center
Building J-17
Wallops Island, VA 23337
Phone: (804) 824-1176

Space Exploration Time Line
1957–1986

1957   *SPUTNIK I* (USSR) **First satellite to orbit** Earth.
         SPUTNIK II (USSR) First satellite to collect biological data from orbit, carried dog.

1958   **EXPLORER I** (USA) First American Earth satellite.
         VANGUARD (USA) First solar-powered satellite.
         SPUTNIK III (USSR) First data about Earth taken from orbit.

1959   *LUNA I* (USSR) First spacecraft to achieve earth-escape velocity, missed moon and went into orbit around the sun.
         PIONEER 4 (USA) First deep-space probe passed within 37,300 mi (59680 km) of moon and goes into solar orbit.
         JUPITER (USA) First primates (two chimpanzees) into space suborbital.
         EXPLORER 6 (USA) First photo of Earth from space.
         LUNA 2 (USSR) First *luna*r probe to impact on moon, no data returned.
         LUNA 3 (USSR) First *luna*r probe to photograph moon's far side (which is never seen from Earth).

1960   **ECHO 1** (USA) First passive (reflector) communications satellite.
         SPUTNIK V (USSR) First recovery of orbited animals from space (two dogs).
         COURIER 18 (USA) First active repeater communications satellite.

1961   **MERCURY 2** (USA) First test of *Mercury*-Redstone flight vehicle with a chimpanzee suborbital.
         VENERA (USSR) Venus probe, passed within 62,000 mi (99,200) of Venus.
         VOSTOK I (USSR) First manned space flight, Yuri Gargarin, 1 orbit.
         MERCURY-FREEDOM 7 (USA) First American manned suborbital flight, Alan Shepard, 15 minutes 22 seconds.
         MERCURY 4 (USA) Gus Grissom, suborbital, capsule sank on return, but astronaut rescued.
         VOSTOK 2 (USSR) Manned space flight, Gherman Titov, 16 orbits, 25 hours.
         MERCURY 5 (USA) First U.S. live orbital flight of chimpanzee recovered, 2 orbits.

1962   **MERCURY-FRIENDSHIP 7** (USA) First U.S. manned orbital flight, John Glenn. 3 orbits, 4 hours, 54 minutes.
         RANGER 4 (USA) First American *luna*r probe to impact on moon, equipment failed, no pictures returned.
         MERCURY 7 (USA) Manned mission, Scott Carpenter, 3 orbits.
         VOSTOK 3 (USSR) Part of first Soviet dual mission (with Vostok 4) A. Nikolayev, 64 orbits, 3 days, 22 hours.
         VOSTOK 4 (USSR) Part of first Soviet dual mission (with Vostok 3), came within 3.1 mi (5 km) of VOSTOK 3 on first orbit P. Popovich, 48 orbits, 2 days, 23 hours.
         MARINER 2 (USA) First successful fly-by of Venus.
         MERCURY 8 (USA) Walter Schirra, 6 orbits, 9 hours.

1963   **MERCURY 9** (USA) First American manned flight to exceed 24 hours, Gordon Cooper, 22 orbits, 34 hours, 20 minutes.
         VOSTOK 5 (USSR) Part of dual mission (with Vostok 6),V. Bykovsky, 81 orbits.

Space Exploration Time Line *(cont.)*

VOSTOK 6 (USSR) Dual mission with Vostok 5, came within 3 mi(5 km) of Vostok 5, Valentina Tereshkova (first woman in space); 48 orbits.

1964   **RANGER 7** (USA) First successful American *luna*r probe; impacted on moon; returned 4,316 close-up photos of *luna*r surface down to impact.
VOSKHOD 1 (USSR) First three-man orbital mission; V. Kamarov, K. Feoktistov, B. Yegerav; 16 orbits.
MARINER 4 (USA) First successful fly-by of Mars.

1965   *VOSKHOD II* (USSR) First space walk; A. Leonov (performed 10-minute EVA. Suit needed to be deflated slightly prior to reentry into spacecraft) P. Belyayev; 17 orbits.
GEMINl 3 (USA) First American 2-man crew; first manned orbital maneuvers; Gus Grissom, John Young; 3 orbits.
GEMINI 4 (USA) First American space walk; Edward White (performed 21-minute EVA); James McDivitt; 62 orbits.
PROTON I (USSR) physics "lab."
GEMINI 5 (USA) First extended manned flight; Gordon Cooper, Charles Conrad; 128 orbits.
VENERA 3 (USSR) impacted Venus March 1, 1966, failed to return data.
GEMINI 6 (USA) and **GEMINI 7** (USA) First meeting of space craft while in orbit; Walter Schirra (6) and Thomas Stafford (7); 16 orbits.

1966   *LUNA 9* (USSR) First soft landing on moon, returned *luna*r-surface photos.
GEMINI 8 (USA) First meeting in space with previously launched target (Agena 11); malfunction caused mission to be ended early; Neil Armstrong, David Scott; 6.5 orbits.
LUNA 10 (USSR) First *luna*r orbiter; returned *luna*r data until May, 1966.
SURVEYOR 1 (USA) First American soft landing on moon; returned 11,240 photos.
GEMINI 9 (USA) Linking with Agena unmanned spacecraft; Thomas Stafford, Eugene Cernan; 2 hours 8 minute EVA by Cernan; 47 orbits.
GEMINI 10 (USA) First use of target vehicle as source of propulsion after meeting and docking in space; first double meeting in space (with Agena 8 and Agena 10); first retrieval of space object (test package of target vehicle) during EVA; John Young, Michael Collins; 43 orbits.
LUNA **ORBITER 1** (USA) orbited moon and returned 297 photos of *luna*r equatorial region as part of program to find landing sites; all orbiters were deliberately crashed on the moon so their radio transmitters would not interfere with later spacecraft.
GEMINI 11 (USA) meeting and docking achieved on first orbit; used Agena 11 propulsion to achieve record altitude of 850 mi (1360 km); Charles Conrad, Richard Gordon; 44 orbits.
GEMINI 12 (USA) Final *Gemini* mission; three EVAs for record total of 5 hours 30 minutes; James Lovell, Buzz Aldrin; 63 orbits.

1967   **APOLLO 1** (USA) Fire inside spacecraft during ground testing resulted in death of three astronauts; Gus Grissom, Edward White, Roger Chaffee.

Space Exploration Time Line (cont.)

SOYUZ 1 (USSR) First manned test flight of new *Soyuz* spacecraft; V. Komarov killed on ground impact when parachute lines of reentry module were fouled.

SURVEYOR 3 (USA) Landed on Moon; took photos made soil analysis.

VENERA 4 (USSR) First successful probe of Venus atmosphere.

LUNA **ORBITER 5** (USA) Photographed five potential *Apollo* landing sites; ended *lunar* orbiter mapping program.

SURVEYOR 6 (USA) performed first rocket lift-off from moon.

APOLLO 4 (USA) First successful unmanned *Apollo* flight.

1968   **APOLL0 5** (USA) First flight of lunar module (unmanned).

ZOND 5 (USSR) First satellite to fly around moon and return to earth.

APOLLO 7 (USA First American 3-man earth orbital mission; Walter Schirra, Don Eisele, Walter Cunningham; 163 orbits.

SOYUZ 2 (USSR) Unmanned satellite; meets target (*Soyuz 3*) in orbit.

SOYUZ 3 (USSR) Manned spacecraft; maneuvered to within 650' (217 m) of *Soyuz 2*; G. Beregovoi; 64 orbits.

ZOND 6 (USSR) Flew around moon, then returned to Earth and landed in USSR.

APOLLO X (USA) First manned orbit of moon; Frank Borman, James Lovell, William Anders; 10 lunar orbits; 6 days, 3 hours.

1969   *SOYUZ 4* (USSR) First docking (with *Soyuz 5*) of two manned Soviet Spacecraft; V. Shatalov, 45 orbits.

SOYUZ 5 (USSR) Docked with *Soyuz 4*; B. Volyanov, A. Yeliseyev, Y. Khrollov; 46 orbits.

MARINER 6 (USA) Flew by Mars on July 31, 1969, sending 75 television pictures.

APOLLO 9 (USA) First test of lunar module in Earth orbit; James McDivitt, David Scott, Russell Schweickart; 151 orbits, 10 days.

APOLLO 10 (USA) First test of lunar module in lunar orbit. Thomas Stafford, Eugene Cernan, John Young, 31 lunar orbits.

APOLLO 11 (USA) First manned lunar landing, first men to walk on moon; NEIL ARMSTRONG, BUZZ ALDRIN, MICHAEL COLLINS; 22 hours on moon with 2 hours, 35 minute EVA by Collins, July 20, 1969.

SOYUZ 6 (USSR) First triple launch (with *Soyuz 7 & 8*) of manned orbit; non-docking group flight; G. Shonin. N. Kubasov, 79 orbits.

SOYUZ 7 (USSR) Target vehicle for group meeting in orbit (with *Soyuz 6 & 8*); A. Filipchenko, V. Volkov, V. Gorbatko; 79 orbits.

SOYUZ 8 (USSR) Flagship in maneuvers (with *Soyuz 6 & 7*); V. Shatalov, A. Yeliseyev; 79 orbits.

APOLLO 12 (USA) Second manned lunar landing, returned parts from *Surveyor 3*; Pete Conrad, Richard Gordon, Alan Bean, 32 hours on moon.

1970   **SERT 2** (USA) First orbital test of electron ion engine.

CHINA 1 (China) First satellite launched by Red China.

APOLLO 13 (USA) Third manned lunar landing attempt, aborted due to oxygen tank explosion. in service module; crew returned safely; James Lovell, Fred Haise, Jack Swigert; 5 days, 22 hours, 53 minutes.

SOYUZ 9 (USSR) Set new duration record for manned space flight; V. Sevastianov, A. Nikolayev; 268 orbits, 17 days, 16 hours, 59 minutes.

Space Exploration Time Line *(cont.)*

LUNA 16 (USSR) First unmanned lunar rover.
VENERA 7 (USSR) Venus atmosphere probe; first successful landing on Venus.

1971   **APOLLO 14** (USA) Third manned lunar landing, collected 96 pounds of lunar samples; Alan Shepard, Stuart Roosa, Edgar Mitchell; 34 hours on moon.
SALYUT I (USSR) Unmanned prototype for orbiting space station and laboratory, fell back to Earth.
SOYUZ 10 (USSR) First crew to dock with orbiting Salyut I, 5 hours 30 minutes; V. Shatalov, A. Yeliseyev, N. Rukavishnikov.
MARS 2 (USSR) First vehicle to land on Mars.
MARINER 9 (USA) First successful Mars orbiter; returned 7,000 pictures of surface.
SOYUZ II (USSR) First crew to occupy Salyut space station (22 days); because of accidental depressurization, cosmonauts died on reentry, G. Dobrovolsky, V. Volkov, V. Patsayey.
APOLLO 15 (USA) Fourth manned lunar-landing, first use of manned Lunar Roving Vehicle; David Scott, Alfred Wordell, James Irwin, 67 hours on moon.

1972   **PIONEER 10** (USA) First successful flyby of Jupiter; First probe to escape solar system.
VENERA 8 (USSR) Transmitted Venus surface data.
APOLLO 16 (USA) Fifth manned lunar landing, collected 213 pounds of lunar samples; Charles Duke, Ken Mattingly, John Young; 71 hours on moon.
ERT 1 (USA) First Earth resource satellite.
APOLLO 17 (USA) Sixth and last *Apollo* manned lunar landing, collected 243 lbs (109 kg) of lunar samples, Eugene Cernan, Ronald Evans, Harrison Schmitt; record 76 hours on moon.

AFTER MOON LANDINGS

1973   **PIONEER 11** (USA) Jupiter probe first successful flyby of Saturn.
SKYLAB (USA) First unmanned space station; placed in Earth orbit, but damaged during launch.
SKYLAB 1 (USA) First crew to occupy *SKYLAB* (28 days); replaced thermal shield and repaired solarwing. Pete Conrad, Joe Kerwin, Paul Weitz.
SKYLAB 2 (USA) Second crew to occupy *SKYLAB* (59.5 days); Alan Bean, Jack Lousma, Owen Garriott.
SOYUZ l2 (USSR) Test of modified spacecraft (chemical batteries replace extendible solar panels) for ferry missions to orbiting Salyut lab; V. Lazarev, O. Makarov.
MARINER 10 (USA) First craft to use gravity of one planet (Venus) to reach another (Mercury), first TV picture of Mercury.
SKYLAB 3 (USA) Third and last crew to occupy *SKYLAB;* longest *SKYLAB* mission (84 days); Gerald Carr, Edward Gibson, William Pogue *(Skylab* was destroyed reentering Earth's atmosphere, July ll, 1979).
SOYUZ 13 (USSR) Manned spacecraft; astrophysical, biological, and earth resources experiments. P. Klilmuk, V. Lebedev; 7 days, 20 hours, 55 minutes.

1974   *SALYUT 3* (USSR) Unmanned space station in orbit 214 days.

Space Exploration Time Line (cont.)

SOYUZ 14 (USSR) Manned spacecraft; crew rendezvoused and docked with *Salyut 3* (14.5 days); P. Popovich, Y. Artyukhin.

SOYUZ 15 (USSR) Manned spacecraft; failed to dock with *Salyut 3*; G. Sarafanov, L. Demir.

SOYUZ 16 (USSR) Manned spacecraft; tested new design for joint USA-USSR Apollo-*Soyuz* test project; A. Flipchenko, N. Rukavishnikov.

1975   **SOYUZ 17** (USSR) Manned spacecraft; crew docked with and occupied *Salyut 4* (28 days); A. Gubarev, G. Grechko.

SOYUZ 18 (USSR) Second crew to occupy *Salyut 4* (63 days) P. Klimuk, V. Sevastyanov.

VENERA 9 (USSR) Venus probe soft-landed and returned first TV pictures from surface.

APOLLO-SOYUZ (USA-USSR) First cooperative international flight; docked in earth orbit for 2 days; T. Stafford, V. Brand, D. Slayton (USA), A. Leonov, and V. Kubasov (USSR).

VIKING 1 (USA) Mars orbiter; first successful Mars landing; returned photographs and data.

VIKING 2 (USA) Mars orbiter landed, returned pictures and data.

SOYUZ 20 (USSR) Unmanned spacecraft; ground-controlled docking with *Salyut 4*.

1976   **SALYUT 5** (USSR) Unmanned space station; orbit 412 days.

SOYUZ 22 (USSR) Manned spacecraft; carried multispectral camera; V. Bykovsky, V. Aksyonov; 7 days, 21 hours, 54 minutes.

SOYUZ 23 (USSR) Manned spacecraft; failed to dock with *Salyut 5*; V. Zudov, V. Rozhdestvensky.

1977 **SOYUZ 24** (USSR) Manned spacecraft; docked with *Salyut 5*; tested and repaired parts aboard space station; V. Gorbatko, Y. Glazkov: 17 days, 16 hours, 8 minutes.

VOYAGER 2 (USA) Fly-by probe of Jupiter, Saturn, Uranus, Neptune; sent back pictures and data until August, 1989.

VOYAGER 1 (USA) Fly-by probe of Jupiter and Saturn; sent back pictures and data on Jupiter and five of its moons and on Saturn and four of its moons.

SALYUT 6 (USSR) Unmanned space station; sent into Earth orbit.

SOYUZ 25 (USSR) Manned spacecraft; failed to dock with *Salyut 6*; V. Kovalenok, V. Ryumin.

SOYUZ 26 (USSR) Manned spacecraft; docked with *Salyut 6*; 1 hour, 28 minutes EVA; Y. Romanenko, G. Grechko; 96 days 10 hours.

1978   **SOYUZ 27** (USSR) Manned spacecraft docked with *Salyut 6*, achieving first three-spacecraft complex (with Salyut 6) V. Dzhanibekov, O. Makarov; 6 days.

PROGRESS 1 (USSR) Unmanned expendable transport craft to resupply *Salyut 6* with propellants, food, and other cargo; on February 7, it was made to reenter the atmosphere and burn up.

SOYUZ 28 (USSR) Manned spacecraft docked with *Salyut 6*; performed 2 hour EVA to replace equipment and retrieve package exposed to space for 10 months; V. Kovalenok, A. Ivanchenkoc; 139 days.

SOYUZ 30 (USSR) Manned spacecraft; international crew; docked with *Salyut 6*; performed biomedical experiments; P. Kimuk, M. Hermanszewski (Poland); 7 days.

Space Exploration Time Line *(cont.)*

PIONEER-VENUS (USA) Five entry probes measure Venus' atmosphere before landing; sent back surface data.

SOYUZ 31 (USSR) Manned spacecraft; international crew docked with *Salyut 6*; V. Bykovsky, S. Jaehn (East Germany); 7 days, 20 hours, 49 minutes.

1979   *SOYUZ 32* (USSR) Seventh crew to occupy *Salyut 6*; deployed radio telescope; V. Lyakhov, V. Ryumin; 175 days.

SOYUZ 33 (USSR) Manned spacecraft; failed to dock with *Salyut 6*; N. Rukavinshnikov, G. Ivanov.

SOYUZ 34 (USSR) Unmanned spacecraft; ground-controlled docking with *Salyut 6* and SOYUZ 32; returned on August 19) with crews from *Soyuz 32*.

SKYLAB fell back to Earth, mostly destroyed by friction of the atmosphere; some large pieces found in Australia, others fell into ocean.

SOYUZ-T (USSR) Unmanned new-generation *Soyuz* craft; ground-controlled docking with *Salyut 6*.

1980   *SOYUZ 35* (USSR) Manned spacecraft; eighth crew to occupy *Salyut 6*; L. Popov, V. Ryumin; 184 days, 20 hours, 12 minutes.

SOYUZ 36 (USSR) Manned spacecraft; international crew docked with *Salyut 6*; V. Kubasov, B. Faukas (Hungary);7 days, 20 hours, 46 minutes.

SOYUZ T-2 (USSR) First manned flight of the *Soyuz T* series; docked with *Salyut 6*, R. Malyshev, V. Aksyonov; 3 days, 22 hours.

SOYUZ 37 (USSR) Manned spacecraft, international crew, docked with *Salyut 6* performed a series of experiments with resident crew (Popov and Ryumin) V. Gorbatko, P. Taun (Vietnam); 7 days, 20 hours, 42 minutes.

SOYUZ 38 (USSR) Manned spacecraft, international crew, ferried fuel and supplies to *Salyut 6*, and returned *Soyuz 3* crew; Y. Romanenko, A. Mendez (Cuba); 7 days, 20 hours, 43 minutes.

SOYUZ T-3 (USSR) Manned spacecraft; first *Soyuz* in nine years to carry three crew members; L. Kizim, G. Strekalov, O. Makarov; 15 days.

1981   *SOYUZ T-4* (USSR) Manned spacecraft; docked with *Salyut 6*; carried out repairs to space station; V. Kovalenok, V. Savinyky; 76 days.

SPACE SHUTTLE COLUMBIA: STS 1 (USA) First orbital flight tested cargo-bay doors; John Young, Robert Crippen; 2 days, 6 hours.

SOYUZ 40 (USSR) Manned spacecraft; docked with *Salyut 6* studied effects on space on construction materials; L. Popov, D. Prunariu (Rumania); 9 days.

STS 2 (USA) Second orbital test flight of *Columbia,* first in-flight test of manipulator arm; Joe Engle, Richard Truly; 2 days, 6 hours.

1982   **STS 3** (USA) Third orbital test flight of Space Shuttle *Columbia;* first manipulation of payload in cargo bay; Jack Lousman, Gordon Fullerton; 8 days.

SALYUT 7 (USSR) Unmanned space station, test of systems and equipment for future crew occupation.

SOYUZ T-6 (USSR) Manned spacecraft; international crew docked with *Salyut 7*; V. Dzhanibekov, A. Ivanchenkoc, J. Chretien (France); 7 days.

Space Exploration Time Line *(cont.)*

STS 4 (USA) Fourth orbital test of Space Shuttle *Columbia;* first commercial experiments and "Getaway Specials;" Ken Mattingly, Henry Hartsfield; 8 days.

SALYUT 7 (USSR) Manned spacecraft first coed crew (2 male, 1 female), docked with SALYUT 7; L. Popov, A. Serebov, S. Savitskaya; 9 days.

STS 5 (USA) Fifth flight of Space Shuttle *Columbia;* first operational manned shuttle flight, launched a pair of commercial satellites; Vance Brand, Robert Overmyer, William Lenor, Joe Allen; 5 days.

1983   **CHALLENGER STS 6** (USA); second shuttle in US fleet; deployed tracking and data relay satellite; Paul Weitz, Karol Bobko, Story Musgrave, Donald Peterson; 5 days.

STS 7 (USA) *Challenger,* first American woman in space; launch of two satellites; first use of remote manipulator arm to release and retrieve payload; Robert Crippen, Fred Hauck, John Fabian, Sally Ride, Norman Thagard; 6 days.

STS 8 (USA) *Challenger;* first night launch and landing; first American black astronaut, launch INSAT 1B satellite: Richard Truly, Daniel Brandenstein, Gulon Bluford, Dale Gardner, William Thorton; 6 days.

STS 9 (USA) *Columbia,* first use of ESA's Spacelab module; first non-American on shuttle; first use of payload specialists; John Young, Brewster Shaw, Owen Garriott, Robert Parker, Byron Lichtenberg, Ulf Merbold (Germany); 10 days.

SOYUZ T-8 (USSR)

SOYUZ T-9 (USSR)

1984   **41B** (USA) *Challenger;* first test of Manned Maneuvering Unit (MMU); launched two satellites; first landing Kennedy Space Center; Vance Bland, Robert (Hoot) Gibson, Ronald McNair, Robert Stewart; 7 days, 23 hours.

41C (USA) *Challenger;* retrieval and repair of Solar Max; EVA by Nelson and van Hoften; launch of Long Duration Exposure Facility (LDEF); Robert Crippen, Francis Scobee, Terry Hart, George Nelson, James van Hoften; 6 days, 23 hours.

41D (USA) *Discovery's* first flight; 32 meter solar array unfolded; launch of three satellites; Henry Hartsfield, Judith Resnick, Charles Walker; 6 days, 56 minutes.

41G (USA) *Challenger;* first EVA by all American woman; satellite refueling tests; launch satellite; Robert Crippen, Jon McBride, David Leestma, Sally Ride, Kathryn Sullivan, Paul Scully-Power, Marc Garneau; eight days.

51A (USA) *Discovery;* retrieval two satellites from faulty orbits; launch of two satellites; Fred Hauck, David Walker, Joe Allen, Anna Fisher, Dale Gardner; 7 days, 23 hours.

SOYUZ T- 10 (USSR)

SOYUZ T- 11 (USSR)

1985   **51C** (USA) *Discovery;* Department of Defense mission; Thomas Mattingly, Loren Shriver, James Buchli, Ellison Onizuka, Gary Payton; 3 days.

51D (USA) *Discovery;* launch two satellites, "Toys in Space" experiments; first US Senator in space; Karol Bobko, Donald Williams, David Griggs, Jeffrey Hoffman, Rhea Seddon, Senator Jake Garn, Charles Walker; 6 days, 23 minutes.

51B (USA) *Challenger;* Spacelab 3, microgravity experiments, biological experiments with monkeys and rats; launch of first "Getaway Special" satellites; Robert Overmyer, Greg Gregory, Don Lind, Norman Thagard, William Thornton, Lodewijk van den Bery, Taylor Wang; 7 days.

51G (USA) *Discovery;* launch three satellites; launch and retrieval of astrophysics payload; Daniel Brandenstein, John Creighton, John Fabian, Shannon Lucid, Steven Nagel, Patrick Baudry, Salman Al-Saud; 7 days.

51F (USA) *Challenger,* Spacelab 2, astronomy experiments, space soda can tests; Challenger "aborts to orbit" after early cutoff of engine; Gordon Fullerton, Roy Bridges, Anthony England, Karl Henize, Story Musgrave, Loren Acton, John-David Barite; 7 days, 22 hours.

511 (USA) *Discovery;* repair and relaunch of satellite; launch of two satellites; Joe Engle, Richard Covey, William Fisher, John Lounge, James van Hoften; 7 days.

51J (USA) Atlantis; first flight of Atlantis, Department of Defense mission; shuttle altitude record of 320 mi(512 km); Karol Bobko, Ronald Grabe, David Hilmers, Robert Stewart, William Pailes; 4 days.

61A (USA) *Challenger;* Spacelab D-1; first control of payload from outside US; first eight-person crew; Henry Hartfield, Steven Nagel, Gulon Bluford, James Buchli, Bonnie Dunbar, Reinhard Furrer, Ernst Messerschmid, Wubbo Ockels; 7 days.

61B (USA) *Atlantis:* EASE/ACCESS beam structure assembly launch of three satellites; Brewster Shaw, Bryan O'Connor, Mary Cleave, Jerry Ross, Sherwood Spring, Rodolfo Neri Vela, Charles Walker; 6 days.

SOYUZ T- 13 (USSR)

SOYUZ T- 14 (USSR)

1986   **61C** (USA) *Columbia;* launch of one satellite; materials science laboratory; first US Representative in space; Robert Gibson, Charles Bolden, Franklin Chang-Diaz, Steven Hawley, George Nelson, Robert Cenker, Rep. Bill Nelson; 6 days.

January 28 Space Shuttle *Challenger* exploded shortly after liftoff; all crew members are lost. Mission objectives included first teacher in space (McAuliffe); launch of two satellites, one to study Halley's Comet; Francis Scobee, Michael Smith, Ronald McNair, Ellison Onizuka, Judith Resnik, Gregory Jarvis, Christa McAuliffe; 74 seconds.

1988 SPACE SHUTTLE *DISCOVERY:* USA IS BACK IN SPACE

Sources of Information:

1957-1983 *Life in Space,* Robert Grant Mason, Time-Life Books, lnc., 1983.
1984-1987 *Odyssey Magazine*, June, 1987.